THE BRACKET CLOCK

Deryck Roberts

THE BRACKET CLOCK

DAVID & CHARLES
Newton Abbot   London   North Pomfret (Vt)

Dedicated to my wife, Jean, for her patience and understanding during the researching and writing of this book, and for her unstinting support for whatever I do; and to David Harker, CMBHI, of Trinity Clocks, Colchester, for his courage in taking on what must have been the oldest apprentice in the business, for his tolerance of my ignorance and, despite the financial pressures and temptations in the antiques trade, for remaining true to his craft and the clocks in his care.

British Library Cataloguing in Publication Data

Roberts, Deryck
  The bracket clock.
  1. Clocks and watches
  I. Title
  681.1′ 13   TS542

  ISBN 0-7153-8261-6

Typeset by Typesetters (Birmingham) Ltd.,
Smethwick, Warley, West Midlands.
and printed in Great Britain
by Butler & Tanner Limited, Frome and London
for David & Charles (Publishers) Limited
Brunel House Newton Abbot Devon

Published in the United States of America
by David & Charles Inc
North Pomfret Vermont 05053 USA

CONTENTS

List of Plates   6

1   The Bracket Clock   7

2   Pre-Bracket Clock Time Measurement   10

3   The Components Come Together   17

4   The Elegant and the Elite, 1700–1750   43

5   A Confusion of Styles, 1750–1800   68

6   Towards and Away From Elegance, 1800–1850   82

7   Consolidation and Competition, 1850–1900   112

8   Decline, Fall and Revival   135

9   Collecting Bracket Clocks   151

    Dating Bracket Clocks   179

    Appendices
      A Fusee design   188
      B Relative power outputs of clock drives   189

    Acknowledgements   190

    Index   191

LIST OF PLATES

1 Front and rear views of a clock by Henry Jones, c1675   45
2 Clock by Daniel Quare, c1700   51
3 Rear of Daniel Quare clock   52
4 Front view of a clock by George Graham, c1720   56
5 Rear view of George Graham clock   57
6 James Markwick clock, c1730   62
7 Front and rear view of a clock by John Rayment, c1760   64
8 John Hedge clock, c1775   77
9 Rear of John Hedge clock   79
10 Hedge and Banister clock, c1810   86
11 Rear of Hedge and Banister clock   87
12 Clock labelled 'Archard', c1817   92
13 Rear view of Archard clock   92
14 Clock by John Cooper, c1825   100
15 Rear view of John Cooper clock   101
16 Clock by Wright of London, c1835   105
17 Clock by Benjamin Vulliamy, c1840   107
18 Clock by Ramsey of Devonport, c1855   113
19 Rear view of Ramsey clock   113
20 Large bracket clock by Rowley, London c1875   117
21 French bracket clock, c1880   119
22 Clock by Winterhalder and Hofmeyer, c1890   123
23 Back of Winterhalder and Hofmeyer clock   123
24 English-made, full-arch clock, c1900   136
25 Rear of full-arch clock   136
26 Lenzkirch domed-top clock, c1910   139
27 Rear of Lenzkirch clock   139
28 German chiming clock   141
29 Five clocks, showing the transition from bracket to mantel clock   143
30 Modern bracket clock by Sinclair, Harding and Bazeley   149

1

THE BRACKET CLOCK

When asked to define a bracket clock, even the expert, sure in his own mind, may hesitate over his terms. A perusal of several books on clocks will reveal the following definitions:

1) Clocks which were intended to be placed on a wall bracket, supplied with the clock for that purpose.
2) A particular style of clock, manufactured from about 1650 to about 1850, anything later being referred to as a mantel clock.
3) A clock with carrying handles on the sides or a single handle at the top.
4) Clocks wherein the movement was attached to the case by two L-shaped brackets.

However, none of the above criteria is entirely satisfactory.

Definition 1 rules out the majority of the beautiful Georgian and Regency clocks usually held up as 'classic' examples of the bracket clock —quite apart from the fact that there are many proud owners who would be astonished and dismayed to have their clocks thus demoted! In fact, as we shall see, a clock supplied with a wall bracket was the exception rather than the rule. The clocks of this particular period, although now included under the generic heading of bracket clocks, were in their day known as table clocks, since they would be placed on a table in the entrance hall, dining-room or withdrawing-room. In support of this argument, such clocks—from their inception until about 1850—almost without exception had a glass panel in the rear door, and quality clocks had a profusely engraved backplate until the end of the eighteenth century, continuing as edge engraving during the first quarter of the nineteenth century.

Such extravagance would have been pointless if the back of the clock was to sit on a wall bracket, out of view. Certainly the finest longcase clocks of the same period never had such decorations: it was assumed that the back of the movement would not be seen. If, however, a clock was placed on a centre table, then the movement would be open to inspection; even if it was placed on a hall table, a mirror on the wall behind it might well show the movement.

Definition 2 depends on one's attitude to clock design and style. There are people who maintain that 'decent' bracket clocks were not made in the years following 1850, that succeeding clocks were the products of mass production. The latter statement is true but it depends on the definition of mass production. Many clocks, dating from 1725 onwards, exhibit a remarkable similarity in, for instance, corner spandrels, hands and even complete cases, suggesting that specialisation in the manufacture of specific components was already accepted by that time. Is not specialisation a form of mass production? Regarding the definition of what is a *decent* clock, terms like 'decent', or 'beautiful' or a 'work of art' are very subjective descriptions, especially when viewed through eyes accustomed to the fashions of the later twentieth century. Clocks in particular, like furniture in general, had their part to play in the evolution of trends in fashion and society and one cannot take their apparent beauty (or the lack of it) out of context. Consider, for example, the surge of mock-Jacobean furnishings during the first quarter of this century. The matching bracket clocks of the period could be considered, from a modern standpoint, as something out of a nightmare, some of them standing over two feet high, all-singing and all-dancing on a choice of bells or gongs. Yet these clocks were sold in quantity and, therefore, were obviously considered as stylish or tasteful in their own time; there is a certain menacing beauty about them!

Definition 3 can be disposed with summarily, otherwise we could call, for example, a carriage clock a bracket clock; it persists, however, in advertisements and auctioneers' catalogues, as if to cast a spell over a would-be buyer.

Definition 4 is plausible when it is realised that the majority of clocks discussed here do indeed have L-shaped mounting brackets between the movement and the case. However, this is not true of every clock; there is for instance a seventeenth-century clock by Fromanteel which is generally accepted as a bracket clock but which lacks these mounting brackets. Many seventeenth-century and early eighteenth-century movements are mounted by screws through the two lower pillars and seat board. This is the least acceptable definition, but I have heard people in the trade defining a clock as a bracket clock because it has these brackets fitted.

So, to discuss the development of this type of clock, a compromise is necessary. If we assume that a bracket clock is:

1 In a case that is basically constructed of wood (except in French clocks)
2 In a case with greater height than width
3 In a case intended to stand on something, not to be freestanding or wall-hung

4 Equipped with a type of movement powered by a spring, not by weights—then we can define our field firmly, excluding metal-cased clocks (including giant carriage clocks), mantel clocks—normally wider than they are high—American weight-driven shelf clocks and others. I have made the exception of French clocks since they have a part to play in the story of the development of bracket clocks from about 1725 onwards. In Edwardian times these clocks were often cased in wood, thus conforming to our definition, but the eponymous eighteenth-century French bracket clock was of gilt metal, often with exotic inlays, such as tortoiseshell; however, a great many of them were designed with matching wall brackets—more often than British clocks were—and for that reason if no other they deserve a mention. Moreover the design of the French bracket clock was copied by English makers in the nineteenth century—especially the 'balloon' case design.

Mantel clocks are the historical successors of bracket clocks, and there were transitional designs, so these will be briefly mentioned. So will the bracket clocks of those countries whose clockmakers influenced developments in Britain—mainly Germany and France, with passing reference to the fringe contributors, Holland and the USA. I hope to demonstrate that some of the clocks competing with those of British makers, especially during the nineteenth century, are worthy of respect; they were examples of workmanship adapted to meet specific markets. English makers, almost without exception, failed to adapt to meet both the markets and the competition in bracket clocks, choosing instead to diversify. I hope that collectors and dealers may have their interest stimulated in these later clocks and gain in appreciation of them: these clocks will be the rarities of the future.

Since London was at the centre of the bracket-clock market, it is common usage to refer to the clocks and their makers as 'English', though of course some were made in other parts of Britain, especially in Scotland.

2
PRE-BRACKET CLOCK TIME MEASUREMENT

When discussing bracket clocks, the only place to start is the second half of the seventeenth century. However, we cannot do this in isolation. Bracket clocks form part of the general development of clocks and time-keeping—indeed with only slight modifications the bracket clock has survived throughout clockmaking's total span, from 1650 to the present —but of course they did not just appear, with all their mechanical components complete. We need to look at how the development of time-keeping technology enabled clockmakers to produce such a small device that was both functional, in terms of accuracy and reliability, and aesthetically pleasing in case and dial design. Every historical topic has its significant dates. The following events and achievements (mainly in mechanical developments) will be described in detail, related to contemporary developments in furniture and fashion.

Before 1000 BC	The sundial applied to time measurement
Before 500 BC	The clepsydra, or water clock in use
AD 300	Sand glasses in use
c1400	Clockmaking in England began
	First domestic clocks
	Verge escapement appeared
1500	The mainspring invented
	Lantern clocks appeared
	'Stackfreed' used to equalise uneven mainspring pull
1550	The fusee in use
1580	Galileo experimented with the pendulum
1656	Huygens and Coster fitted the pendulum to a domestic clock
1658	Fromanteel introduced the pendulum to England
1665	Bracket clocks begin their development
1666	The recoil escapement invented
1675	Edward Barlow invented the rack-striking mechanism
1685	'Bolt-and-shutter' maintaining power in use

1715	George Graham invented the 'dead-beat' escapement
1725	George Harrison's 'grid-iron' pendulum for temperature compensation invented
1760	Enamelled dial appeared on bracket clocks Competition from French bracket clocks increasing
1800	Onset of mass-production methods of clockmaking
1830	Introduction of the coiled-tape gong in striking mechanisms
1840	Bain made the first electric clock
1859	The Great Clock of Westminster fostered the popularity of chiming clocks
1870	Competition from Germany began to take effect English makers diversified
1880	Transition from bracket clock to mantel clock began
1904	Guillaume invented the 'invar' alloy for temperature-compensated pendulums
1921	The quartz crystal clock developed
1955	Atomic clock invented

One does not need to go into realms of higher mathematics to understand that man cannot *control* time, the best we can do being to *measure* it as accurately as developments in technology allow—and use that measurement to control our actions. The problems of measurement are increased by the fact that we compete with the vagaries of natural forces—heat, cold, vibration, gravity and the normal mechanical inaccuracies of manufactured components. These are real problems as far as bracket clocks are concerned and we shall see how the clockmakers attempted to solve them. Also, of course, we attempt to rationalise natural time into neat divisions of hours, minutes and seconds—divisions which do not occur in a natural cycle. Modern chronological accuracy tends to be concerned with absolute timing for use in governing our space-age lives, and in the latter part of the twentieth century we have clocks with an absolute accuracy of at least one-thousandth of a second. With bracket clocks we are not interested in such degrees of accuracy; we are discussing mechanical clocks of a type that can never approach it and have no reason to do so. A typical bracket clock of the late seventeenth century would be no more accurate than plus or minus a few minutes a week and a top-quality, regulator-type bracket clock of the early nineteenth century might manage an accuracy of plus or minus a few seconds a week—adequate for most domestic purposes. The pathway to an accuracy of even minutes per week was a long and difficult one. Man had to start with what he then thought was the only fixed object in the firmament—the sun. Unfortunately he soon discovered that the solar day (or more correctly, the 'tropical' day) is not a fixed unit of time; because of several influences, such as the earth's elliptical rather than circular orbit, and a constant tilting of its axis, as well as a 'wobble' caused by the attraction of the larger nearby planets, the time for the sun to traverse a meridian varies, from minus about fourteen minutes in spring to plus about sixteen minutes in autumn, say roughly a quarter of an hour difference from the 'mean' time. In fact the mean time coincides with the solar time on only four occasions a year; at the two periods known as the spring and autumn equinox (from the latin *equi*, equal, *nox*, night), when the sun crosses the equator, and when the sun is at its furthest point from the equator, during the summer and winter solstice. Thus the divisions on a sundial are not of equal distance, but must accommodate a shifting variation. For accurate measurement solar time is inadequate, and astronomers rely on the more accurate event of the earth's rotation on its axis in relation to the fixed stars—this is known as sidereal time.

To add to measurement problems, there are two further considerations. The first is the variation in the earth's magnetic pole; this is of more direct interest to navigation timing problems than to domestic clock timing. The more immediate problem is of course that, as the early astronomers realised, one year does not have quite 365 days and nights. In our standard 'year', the earth makes 366 revolutions if measured in true, sidereal time; in mean or solar time, this is equal to 365 days, 6 hours and 10 minutes—an inconvenient difference difficult to accommodate in a clock mechanism. In practice we have rationalised this variance, since the time of the Roman Empire, by counting the year as 365 days, adding a complete day when necessary. Thus, ignoring the odd minutes, the six hours' difference each year adds up to a twenty-four hour day once every four years. This is convenient for a clock mechanism, but we cannot ignore totally those odd minutes and seconds, which over several hundred years would grow to significant proportions. To solve this problem in a practical (if not mathematically perfect) way, Pope Gregory XII decreed in 1582 that the then-accumulated error of ten days should be struck from the calendar, and that to compensate in the future, three leap years should be omitted in every 400 years. The present generation will not witness this momentous event, since the year 2000 is the fourth year in the series, and is therefore still a leap year.

England did not adopt the Gregorian calendar until 1752, by which time the error was eleven days; the last nation to adopt the calendar was the USSR, as late as 1917 when the error had accumulated to thirteen days. The rationalisation had at least given us a day and night of fixed length (except for the more recent custom of setting the nation's clocks backwards and then forwards one hour each year!) but for clock purposes this fixed time had to be subdivided into units that would be useful in everyday life. At this time the pace of life was not critical, within minutes; indeed lantern clocks of the seventeenth and early eighteenth century often had only an hour hand. That was not simply because the mechanism was not accurate enough to require a minute hand; the single hand persisted on provincial longcase clocks until well into the eighteenth century and certainly until after the time when clocks could keep accurate time to within one minute a *week*.

The exact reason why the time period was divided into twenty-four is a matter of continuing speculation and research. Certainly the timing systems so far discovered were based on what we would now call a twenty-four-hour cycle, but having said that a certain amount of confusion (or obstinacy) reigned. It seems logical that the science of timing developed simultaneously within several civilisations; but what is important is that the systems all used a twenty-four-hour cycle. In Nuremburg, for example, the public clocks of the sixteenth century divided the time into equal hours, but had unequal periods of night and day (except at the equinox); this meant that night and day times had to be manually adjusted as the year progressed. Apart from confusing the immediate population, the Nuremburg system was out of step with European neighbours, who had adopted the equal hours, equal periods, idea. Probably Nuremburg, being the accepted birthplace of clockmaking in northern Europe, had to suffer the usual reward of the innovator—being saddled with a new and therefore imperfect system whilst later followers could analyse and avoid the initial errors.

Italy had similar problems. In the fourteenth century, for example, the clock systems developed were mostly within the monasteries. The early clocks, of the turret type, did not have bells or dials, but had possibly a small device that rang a bell as the hour approached, similar to the 'passing' strike on some skeleton clocks. This acted as a warning to the keeper, who then rang a bell to signal the beginning of a canonical period, or chapter; the bell would be of little use to the general public since it rang a 'code' for the particular chapter, and not the actual number of hours. Later, it appears, the ringing was extended to sound the chapter code for the monks and the hours for the general populace. How this was achieved in practice is puzzling, since canonical 'hours' were not necessarily in phase with solar hours. Our present-day terminology retains a link with these early monastic clocks, since the circle whereon the hours and minutes are marked is known as the 'chapter' ring. The chapter was a short lesson, read in Latin, which was part of a cycle of prayer; it appears in the English language as 'a division of a whole' in the fifteenth century, perhaps—but not certainly—deriving from the monastic source. The chapter ring therefore is an apt name for a device to divide up the cycle of twelve (or twenty-four) hours.

During the fourteenth and fifteenth centuries, in Europe, two innovations came into common use. The first was the clock dial, initially a rotating dial with a fixed pointer to indicate the hours, and later a fixed dial with the pointer, driven by gearing, rotating around it. It is likely that in these early clocks the drive was by weights through a 'foliot' or 'balance-wheel' escapement—the escapements used in bracket clocks are explained in the next chapter. The first dials were of the twenty-four-hour type which survived in the country districts of Italy until well into the nineteenth century—and here Italy was left with the same problem as Nuremberg: the twenty-four-hour dial was adequate, but the number of blows struck by the bell was excessive, requiring a substantial amount of power and being more prone to inaccuracies through errors in counting.

The second, and more important, innovation was that of the automatic striking mechanism. We are not certain who invented it, but we do know it was of the 'count-wheel' or 'locking-plate' type (see next chapter).

Thus, as we move into the sixteenth century, we have at least the rudiments of a clock, a weight-driven mechanism with an escapement, a single hour hand, a striking mechanism and a dial to record the hours. We have still some way to go before we can see a recognisable bracket clock—at least twenty-five years before we see evidence of a clock driven by spring power instead of weight-and-gravity, and the same period, therefore, before the clock could be made small enough to fit into a domestic site. Not for over one hundred years would the pendulum be in action, followed by the development of a minute hand to exploit the new accuracy the pendulum brought. It would still be many years before the man in the street could go to a clockmaker to purchase a clock. He had to make do with the latest line in the oldest time-recorders known, the sundial and the sand glass (the more usual devices found in England), the water clock or clepsydra (found in Greece, the Middle and Far East) and the 'destructive' timetelling devices (used in Europe and the Far East). The latter were not such dramatic devices as they sound, being merely systems of indicating the passing of time by the burning of a candle or a small quantity of oil.

The intricacies of these devices are not for this book, but the clepsydra and the sand glass in particular met some of the same problems caused by natural forces and mechanical inaccuracies that later faced the makers of the early bracket clocks. To consider the clepsydra and the sand glass

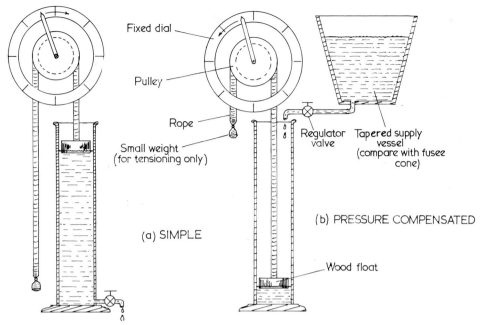

Figure 1   The clepsydra

together, as a similar device, the main problem is to achieve an even flow of material, since this flow is the timing mechanism. If we take a simple cylinder, as shown in figure 1a, fit a valve to restrict the output, and fill it with water or sand, we have a timing device. In a simple clepsydra, a float within the cylinder, coupled to a thin rope running over a pulley, will allow us to measure the time; a pointer fixed to the pulley could revolve within a dial, and this dial, although it is actually measuring water loss, can be calibrated to measure time. If, instead, the cylinder is filled with sand, lines can be scribed across the cylinder to indicate the time taken for the sand to be released. This simple system cannot give a constant measurement: the amount of material flowing from the output decreases as the level of that still in the cylinder decreases. In engineering terms we are concerned with the pressure exerted by a head of fluid—be it water or sand. The direct analogy is the effect on your bathroom shower if you raise the height of the water supply tank—the higher it is, the more pressure you have at the shower head. If the water in the supply tank was allowed to fall sufficiently, you would notice the intensity of the shower also falling.

One way of solving this problem would be to have a decreasing interval between the hour markings on the clepsydra, or between the lines scribed on the sand glass, but this is not very satisfactory. The practical answer is to design the cylinder so that as the pressure head decreases, the amount of material flowing through the output also decreases: in other words, reshape the cylinder into a conical form, as shown in figure 1b. This allows a constant fall in the level of the material. The clepsydra dial or the sand glass can then be marked with uniform spacings.

It is worth dwelling on this point, because the makers of the first spring-driven clock were faced with a similar problem—except that with the clepsydra it is caused by weight and in the clock it is caused by the force created by a tightly coiled spring. As we shall see, a similar effect occurs with the spring, and the solution is to use a conical device, the fusee, discussed later. Compare the shape of this fusee (see figure 3, page 24) with the shape of the clepsydra in figure 1b and the shape of a sand glass. The conical shape holds the answer, whether the problem is one of gravity or of spring power. (It is a simple and fascinating task to build a clepsydra of the type shown in figure 1b; it will not be as accurate as your digital wristwatch but it's a lot more fun!)

In practice, of course, the sand glass was generally used to measure a fixed amount of time—as in today's eggtimer—so the job of designing the correct form of cone was much simpler: the cylinder could be filled with the right weight of sand, determined by trial and error. The basic drawback to both systems is that they will only record a relatively short period of time before having to be recharged, the clepsydra being refilled with water and the sand glass inverted. But for the ordinary people such simple timing devices lingered on well into the eighteenth century, although clocks were well developed by then. The turret clock, at least, was fairly common in the civilised world by the beginning of the sixteenth century. The rudiments of the domestic clock were there: what was needed was a further combination of circumstance and ingenuity, the serendipity of the clock scene.

3

THE COMPONENTS COME TOGETHER

In its simplest form a clock consists of two elements: a power source and a control system. Here we look at the problems with, and the development of, both the power source (ultimately the spring) and the control system (the pendulum and the various forms of escapement). Those natural problems of heat and cold, vibration and gravity, and the mechanical problems of manufactured components have been mentioned earlier; they were to cause severe temporary setbacks to the early clockmakers, affecting both the power source and the control system—especially when the clock must be small enough to fit into a normal house, and even more acutely when the clock had to be portable.

The simplest source of power to drive a clock is the falling of a weight under gravity, the prime advantage of this system being that it generates a *constant* force. Unfortunately, for a bracket clock of normal dimensions a weight drive is little use, as there is not enough height available for a weight to fall any significant distance. In a longcase clock or a hooded wall clock (forerunner of the longcase) this is no problem, since there is usually a clear space of about five or six feet in which a weight can be allowed to fall. But the early longcase might remain in one position for most of its working life; the bracket clock was usually intended to be carried from room to room. Weights clanking around inside the case would do no good to the clock or the owner's nerves.

The much-sought alternative to the weight drive is of course the spring drive. I say 'of course' since in the twentieth century the spring is an intrinsic part of our lives, found in so many of the industrial and domestic products around us. But like the majority of simple, efficient devices, it is only obvious because somebody thought of it first.

A spring is a means of storing and releasing energy, its function equivalent to that of a falling weight, but there the simple analogy ends. The main disadvantage with a standard spring of any design is that its available force is not constant throughout its range ('non-linear' in engineering terms). If a coiled, flat spring of the type used in a clock is wound up to, say, half its possible 'tightness', a certain force will be generated once the winder is released; however, that force will increase if the spring is wound further, reaching a maximum when the spring is fully coiled. This is not suitable for a clock. If we assume that the clock mechanism is a constant load to be overcome by the spring (which to all intents it is), then it will be driven at a speed relative to the force applied by the spring—the clock mechanism will revolve quickly when the spring is fully wound and more slowly as the spring uncoils and its available force decreases.

This problem of a non-constant force is inherent in all springs of the flat, coiled type, as it is impossible to design a practical spring that gives a constant force over a wide range of operation. With today's technology, a spring that will be linear over a small part of its total range can be made, but that part is too small to be any use in a clock spring; not much can be done to even out the force exerted by the spring at the extreme ends of its range, fully uncoiled and fully coiled.

The most practical demonstration of the spring's characteristics under almost natural conditions can be found in the cheaper range of German or American clocks of the nineteenth century. I own an American 'drop dial' wall clock, made around 1890, with an attractive inlaid case but with a very mass-produced eight-day movement. The springs on this clock, as on many shelf, bracket and mantel clocks, are simply attached, one end to the winding arbor, the other end to one of the pillars separating the two plates. When the clock is fully wound, it will start to gain, becoming about two minutes fast towards the middle of its total duration, when the spring is still coiled fairly closely. From that point, it will start to lose time, ending up about three minutes slow after seven days. (It may be happy coincidence *or* design that the net result is only a one-minute deviation in seven days.) However, if the clock is left to run on beyond the seven days, it will start to lose time fairly rapidly; in theory it would continue to lose time at an ever-increasing rate. In practice, the outer coil of the spring comes up against one of the pillars and cannot uncoil completely; the clock stops after eight days.

In these clocks the springs are working over (almost) their whole range, but this is not so with most clocks. One way to prevent the spring from uncoiling completely is to enclose it in a metal tube (the 'barrel' in horological terminology) so that it is prevented from uncoiling by coming into contact with the inside of the barrel; the clockmaker must ensure that in doing this he can still get enough turns on the spring to give the required duration of power. A study of any French bracket clock of the eighteenth, nineteenth and early twentieth centuries, or a good-quality movement from a German bracket clock of the nineteenth and early twentieth century, or an English mantel clock or transition (from bracket to mantel) clock of the late nineteenth and early twentieth century, will reveal these spring barrels, completely enclosing the spring itself. On average these clocks perform acceptably, since they are using only part of the total range of the spring; but they are not accurate, because they still use power from a fully-coiled spring of sufficient strength to run for the usual eight days.

One answer to this problem is to use a longer spring of weak power—in other words, to use many more turns of the spring, in conjunction with a delicate, light-running movement. This kind of spring would give a much more constant force than a stronger one can give. The theory could be taken to ridiculous extremes by having a spring that required several hundred turns from fully uncoiled to fully coiled, but although that would achieve almost a constant force, the power available would be so small that it wouldn't drive the clock mechanism! However, the French clocks, including the bracket clocks, used this idea to good effect right through the eighteenth, nineteenth and twentieth centuries up to the present day—a long spring, weak enough to give a reasonably constant force, driving a lightweight movement, with the spring enclosed in a barrel. Take a clock of this type, perhaps one that is a hundred years old, and you will find that although it requires a few more turns of the winding key than an English, German or American clock, it will keep good time to within less than a minute a week (if it is in good repair), and it will moreover run for about fourteen days. After ten days or so it will start to lose time, but since most clocks are wound up once a week, this is unimportant. What is important is the fact that the French clocks of this type, with their high-quality, small but relatively cheap design, posed a serious threat to the product of the English clockmakers. That story will unfold as we examine the development of the bracket clock. But we must first examine how the clockmakers solved the problem of the non-linear spring.

The inventor of the spring-driven clock, who as yet remains an unidentified hero of the last half of the fifteenth century, must have thought he had hit the jackpot. He had succeeded in making a clock that could be placed on a table and could also be carried from room to room; as Ralph Waldo Emerson said, 'If a man make a better mousetrap than his neighbour, though he build his house in the woods, the world will make a beaten path to his door.' This may have happened in Southern Europe, when news of a spring-driven clock was broadcast.

However, as we now know, the simple spring, especially that of the fifteenth century, is not accurate enough to compete with a weight-driven mechanism. The early springs had to be made from a thin rod of steel, beaten out into a flat strip; as such springs would be liable to fracture if then forced into a coil shape, they then had to be hardened and tempered, involving in those days heating the steel to a temperature over 400°C, then quenching it in oil to achieve a surface hardness; springs would then be allowed to soak in the furnace at a temperature of 150°C, to relieve any stress in the metal caused by hammering it into strip form. Even then the problems were not completely eradicated. A spring put into service in a clock could still fail, due to one of the following reasons:

(a)   'Decarburisation' due to poor tempering or annealing: this is where the carbon content, on which the spring relies for its durability, is lowered by errors in the manufacturing process. The spring will eventually 'fatigue', an engineering term which describes the condition beautifully, since the spring soon gets tired! Generally, the higher the carbon content, the tougher the spring will be; examples are the masonry-drill bit, or surgical implements, which must have some 'spring' while retaining their strength. Nowadays, of course, we use more exotic alloys, such as chrome, vanadium and tungsten, to achieve a similar but improved metal.

(b)   Over-stretching of the molecules of the steel during the forming process.

(c)   Fracture of the molecules during forming process.

(d)   Mechanical damage during forming, fitting or operation. The strip of steel could develop a hairline crack while being hammered, probably revealing itself only when the mechanism was wound up to its full extent for the first time. Scratching or scoring during the drilling of the two locating holes could cause eventual fracture, especially if the holes had even a suspicion of a sharp edge.

A word of warning is useful here, since many spring breakages today can be traced to faults in the area around these holes. If a spring should break within a few inches of one extremity, it is often possible to repair it by cutting off the damaged piece and forming a new location hole. If you examine a correct spring, you will see that the end looks like the example shown in fig 2a: the end of the strip is rounded, and the locating hole (to

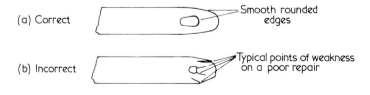

Figure 2   Spring ends

grip the projection on the centre shaft or the arbor, or the projection on the inside of the barrel, depending on which end of the spring we are considering) is well formed, usually pear-shaped to create a wedge effect, and with all the sharp edges filed smooth. Ideally, the whole spring will be re-hardened and tempered. What it should *not* look like is the example shown in fig 2b, where a suspicion of a sharp edge will eventually lead to a crack developing. Again, the spring can be repaired by placing it in a vice and drilling a new hole, subjecting the last few inches of the spring to the possibility of damage through rough handling.

A further complication can arise if the spring barrel itself has been damaged on the inside surface; the coils of the spring will grind against any burr and eventually a groove will be worn in the spring strip, or it will 'snag' against the burr, causing a crack to develop. In any case, the end result will be the same. It is possible to repair the outer end of the spring, but, because of its position, the inner end presents severe difficulties.

The early spring makers had all these problems to overcome and for every spring fitted into a clock there must have been several rejects. However, the necessary skill was there: blacksmiths, especially in Italy, had been making swords in this way for many years.

The problem, of course, did not end with the fitting of the spring. The need for a constant force on the clock train of gears remained the crux of the matter, because in its simplest form a clock can be considered as an engine—the controlled release of the spring drives the gears and, ultimately, the hands of the clock. It is not a simple engine, since the regular rotation of the gear keeps being stopped by the escapement—the thing that produces the tick. However, as we shall see in the section on escapements, the constant force is still necessary.

The clockmakers' first solution to the problem was the stackfreed. This does not much concern us here, since it was never fitted into what is usually recognised as a bracket clock—indeed, as far as I know it was only used in Germany. The mainspring arbor was geared to an auxiliary arbor, fitted with a cam, on to which a stiff spring was bearing. In principle, when the spring was fully coiled, and exerting maximum force, it would be bearing on the high-lift section of the cam, exerting a greater resistance to the rotation of the arbor; as the mainspring uncoiled, the stiff spring would exert a decreasing resistance as the cam lift decreased. The auxiliary arbor would of course be geared to rotate through one revolution during the total uncoiling of the mainspring.

But the device that solved the problem was the fusee. It remained the means of overcoming the non-linear spring force, and was used in bracket clocks from the middle of the seventeenth century until the late nineteenth century, when technology and the price war made it redundant. Indeed the fusee is retained in modern reproductions, especially those in which the movement is on show, such as 'skeleton' clocks. It must be said, though, that with modern spring design the fusee is retained more for its aesthetic appeal than for its functional qualities.

The term fusee is said to come from the Latin *fusata*, a tapered spindle on which strands of wool were wound before weaving. The spindle was grooved in the form of a screw thread, and tapered so that the strands would run up the cone, filling the spindle evenly instead of bunching. Exactly how the name acquired its French spelling is a mystery, although in France the term did appear to refer to that same spindle of wool. Certainly the fusee was rarely if ever used in French clocks, and never in French bracket clocks unless it was to special order, or the work of an English clockmaker working in France.

The earliest example of the fusee, as far as we know, appears in a clock by Jacob of Prague in the first quarter of the sixteenth century. (The clock is dated 1525, but like many long-revered sacred cows this is now questioned.) Whatever the date, it seems likely that the fusee was first introduced in Germany, which as well as the public clocks in Nuremburg already mentioned had other established clockmaking centres in the sixteenth century; they produced, amongst other items, some simple versions of a table clock, the forerunner of the bracket clock.

The reader may, incidentally, ask incredulously whether the fusee was actually the one device not invented by Leonardo da Vinci. Relax! A drawing of an engine made around the end of the fifteenth century depicts a device that is almost certainly a fusee, although as far as is known da Vinci never used one in a clock.

The operation of a fusee is complicated in terms of engineering calculations, but simple to harness effectively. The non-linear force produced by the spring is observed as a rotary force driving the first gear (known as the 'great' wheel in clock terms) of a number, or train, of gears. This force is called a 'torque' in engineering terms and is the rotary equivalent of that most ancient tool, the lever. The same thing is demonstrated in, say, the tightening of a car's wheel-nuts. A mechanic using a normal-length spanner cannot tighten them enough to ensure they will not come loose under the stresses imposed on the wheel. He can do so if he uses a longer spanner, such as the usual 'spider'. We say that he is obtaining extra torque, the turning force on the nut. This analogy of the lever can be used to demonstrate the effect of the fusee. The smaller-diameter end of the fusee, when pulled by the fusee line, exerts a torque equal to the spring strength times the radius of the fusee cone at that point. Since the fusee line is wound on from the larger-diameter end, the spring strength will be at its maximum when the line reaches the smaller end. Thus the stronger spring force is acting over a lesser length of lever (the smaller radius of the cone), and the weaker spring force is acting over the greater length of lever (the larger radius of the cone). In the ideal example, the resulting torque would be constant over the whole length of the fusee cone. To achieve this we should take a point halfway between the maximum and minimum force exerted by the spring, and decide on the diameter of the fusee there, bearing in mind the physical constraints of fitting the fusee into the clock; this multiplication of force and distance gives our datum for the remainder of the calculations. Then taking our measurements of spring force, we can calculate the diameter of the fusee at any given point that will result in a constant torque. We have solved the problem!

To those who are familiar with the fusee, my apologies for this long explanation of its action; but I have found that even experienced collectors and dealers (and some repairers) who know why a fusee is needed often cannot explain how it works. For anyone who would like to pursue the matter a little further, I have detailed on page 188 the design of a fusee relative to its spring. For comparison, page 189 shows the torque supplied by: a fusee drive from an English bracket clock; a spring and barrel drive from a French bracket clock; and an 'open' spring drive from an American (Ansonia Clock Company) mantel or shelf clock. The graph is a diagrammatic representation only, since the length and the power of these springs vary greatly.

The flexible connection between the fusee itself and the spring barrel was originally a line made from natural gut, with the inherent drawbacks of a natural product—inconsistency of diameter and an unpredictable amount of stretch. During the later eighteenth century a link chain was

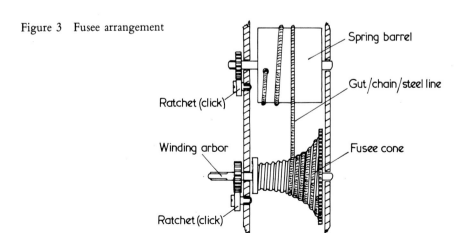

Figure 3   Fusee arrangement

Spring barrel

Gut/chain/steel line

Ratchet (click)

Winding arbor

Fusee cone

Ratchet (click)

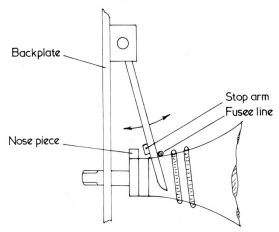

Figure 4   Fusee stopwork

Backplate

Stop arm
Fusee line

Nose piece

introduced, following its proved success in watches, and in the nineteenth century came multi-strand wire cable. Should you find a clock with its lines missing, or tampered with, it is óften possible to ascertain what the original line would have been. If it was a chain, the barrel will have a single slot to receive the chain hook, and the fusee cone will be cut with a square-section groove. For gut or wire lines, the barrel will have three holes, through which the line end is knotted, and the fusee will have a half-round section groove. Beyond this it is difficult to find further clues, except that if the barrel has heavy wear-marks the line was probably a wire.

In practice the fusee has a further two refinements. The first is a simple device to prevent the overwinding of the line on the fusee cone and its consequently becoming entangled round the shaft or arbor. Figure 4 shows how the device operates. The line winds on to the fusee cone, starting (as we now know) at the large-diameter end where the spring strength is least. As winding is almost completed, the line comes into contact with a spring-loaded arm, which is pushed towards the narrow end of the fusee cone as the line continues to be wound. Once the line has reached the narrow end, this arm comes into solid contact with the 'nose piece', a projection on the end of the fusee preventing any further winding. The overall device is usually known as 'stop-work'; the early clockmakers sometimes referred to it as the 'garde-gut', a more profound description since the device would prevent an over-enthusiastic owner from breaking the gut line!

The second refinement is concerned with the spring barrel. One problem in using a flexible connection of any kind is that unless a constant tension is maintained on the line, it may slip off the threads of the fusee cone. To maintain some tension the spring barrel is 'set-up': with all the line wound on the spring barrel and connected to the fusee cone, the spring barrel itself is turned against its own ratchet system, putting a tension in the line. Thus, when the line is wound on to the fusee cone, and then allowed to run off the cone as the clock runs down, there is still some tension on the fusee line when the clock stops. The pre-setting of this tension is an empirical decision today. 'Sufficient' will suffice—one old clockmaker of my acquaintance always sets up the tension as 'one click for each day of the week'; in other words, he counts seven clicks of the spring-barrel ratchet. In the early days of unpredictable springs and poor escapements this setting-up was used also to regulate the clock—varying the initial tension varies the power *range* of the spring; but it is not necessary to do this today.

We now have a complete power system for the clock, a system that with a few modifications has survived for 400 years of clockmaking, and one that will continue to survive, if only for its initial beauty.

CONTROL SYSTEM

The power system is of little use on its own, of course. If you were to wind up a spring system, connected to a train of gears and ultimately to a pair of clock hands, on releasing the key the mechanism would revolve at a frightening speed. Even if the gear train survived this shock, the period from the spring being fully wound to unwound would be a matter of minutes—not much use as a time recorder! What we need is some device that releases the spring force at a regular, relatively slow speed which, when combined with suitable gearing, will result in the two shafts holding the clock hands rotating at a speed that will record the passage of time—or as near to natural time as we need. In practice this device consists of two components, the pendulum and the escapement.

The pendulum
To those familiar with the development of clocks in general, it may seem wrong to deal with the pendulum first. The escapement *must* have been fitted to the earliest clock ever made—before the fourteenth century—otherwise the clock would not have functioned as a clock; pendulum control did not arrive until the seventeenth century. The 'foliot' device, or sometimes the 'balance wheel', the forerunner of the escapement used in modern clocks and watches, was used first in turret clocks and later in domestic table clocks. These devices were notoriously inaccurate, however, being especially susceptible to quite small changes in driving force and, to a lesser extent, to environmental conditions, including changes in temperature. They were not used in bracket clocks as we know them, and the balance wheel was not revived generally for use in

domestic clocks until the middle of the nineteenth century, by which time developments in technology, especially in marine chronology, had solved the initial problems . (A more detailed description of these devices may be found in books covering the overall development of timekeeping, such as Anthony Bird's *English House Clocks, 1600–1850.*)

When one considers a pendulum, especially that of a longcase clock, swinging in its rhythmical, almost magical, way, one instinctively feels that like so many simple and magnificent ideas it must have come from the mind of a da Vinci or a Galileo. Instinct is correct. In the sixteenth century Galileo the elder had watched the motion of a hanging lamp in the cathedral at Pisa. The story goes that the suspension chain had been disturbed, perhaps as the lamp was lit before the service, and Galileo saw that while the lamp's swing decreased in length and finally stopped altogether, the lamp took the same amount of time to swing through each arc. The observation was not accurate, at that stage, as he had only his own pulse available as means of timing. (We may reflect on the quality of the sermon if his pulse rate did not vary throughout the service.) However, Galileo had discovered that, for a given length, a pendulum will take the same time to swing through its arc, even though that arc will decrease if, after the initial disturbance, the pendulum is left to its own devices. In other words, a pendulum is isochronous (from the Greek *iso*, equal, *chronos*, time).

The simple pendulum will always come to rest eventually, because of the combined effects of friction on the suspension, the resistance of the air as the pendulum-bob cuts through it, and the inevitable force of gravity, which will act to bring the pendulum into a vertical position. During the next fifty years, Galileo and others used the pendulum phenomenon in the timing of astronomical observations, although the method of keeping the pendulum swinging was a little crude—the bob was given a slight push once the arc of the swing had decreased. One significant discovery was that the effect of gravity had to be taken into account when calculating the swing, or periodic time, of a pendulum; the early observers realised that the gravitational effect varies depending on where you are on the earth's surface—it is most at the equator, diminishing towards the poles. Also, if you take a pendulum that is 40 inches long and find that it 'beats' 1 second, it will not beat half-a-second if you halve the length. The time, in fact, varies as the square root of the length, the equation being:

$$T \text{ (period of time)} = 2\,\pi\sqrt{\frac{l \text{ (effective length)}}{g \text{ (gravity)}}}$$

In England, the one-second pendulum, or 'royal' pendulum, used in longcase clocks, is therefore 39.107 inches; the effective length is a little complicated to determine, but for practical purposes can be taken as the distance from the point of suspension to the centre of the pendulum bob. Therefore, in a bracket-clock case of 'average' height, say 15 inches, the longest pendulum that will fit into the case is about 10 inches. So:

$$T \text{ (period of time)} = 2\pi\sqrt{\frac{l}{g}}$$

$$= 3.142$$
$$l = 10 \text{ inches}$$
$$g = (32.2 \times 12) = 386.4 \text{ inches/sec/sec.}$$

$$T = (2 \times 3.142)\sqrt{\frac{10}{386.4}} = 1.01 \text{ total period.}$$

We call this a 'half-second' pendulum, since in clocks we count from one beat to the next (or from the limit of one swing to the limit of the return swing), whereas the total time period is from the limit of one swing, to the limit of the return swing *and back again*.

Galileo sketched designs of a pendulum applied to a clock mechanism, but being old and nearly blind by 1640 he left it to his son Vincenzo to translate the designs into hardware. For one reason or another, the clock was never finished. A model to this design may be seen in the Science Museum, London, however, from which we can see that such a clock would have been a viable proposition. The application of the pendulum was left to Christian Huygens van Zulichem, a Dutch scientist and astronomer, who in 1656 converted a turret clock to pendulum operation. Huygens also discovered that a pendulum is *not* truly isochronous; as the arc increases, the pendulum rod reaches a point where it must, in theory, begin to reduce its length in order to remain as a true pendulum. Obviously, with a normal pendulum rod, it is not possible to do this.

Without delving into the mechanics of this, the effect can be demonstrated. If you take a piece of cord with a weight attached, and start it swinging in a small arc, it will act like a pendulum; now increase the swing, until the arc is about 90°, and you will notice that at the limit of the swing the cord will lose its tension, the weight dropping vertically until the cord is tensioned once more. This effect will increase until, with the arc at about 150°, a pendulum action becomes impossible; you can imagine, however, that if you could move your hand (the suspension point) away from the weight in an accurate and controlled fashion, moving it back again as the weight started its return swing, it would still perform as a pendulum. This is not an absolutely correct analogy, but it demontrates the principle.

This effect begins, in fact, at relatively low degrees of arc, as Huygens discovered—low enough to affect the accuracy of a pendulum using the existing forms of escapement. Huygens attempted, not wholly success-fully, to solve the problem by using 'cycloidal' cheeks, fitted close to the suspension point. As the pendulum approached this non-isochronous zone, the pendulum strip would contact these cheeks and be forced to follow a 'false' curve. The idea was good, if one is thinking of a regulator clock of extreme accuracy; but for a domestic clock, especially a bracket clock with its relatively small pendulum movement, the system is an unwarranted expense. English clockmakers never used it, and it appeared in only a minute number of bracket clocks.

Whatever its scientific problems, the pendulum offered clockmakers a great step forward, especially in its potential application to bracket clocks. Its introduction to Britain set the pattern of design for the next 200 years of bracket-clock development. It was probably first brought in by that prestigious Anglo-Dutch clockmaking family, the Fromanteels. When Ahasuerus Fromanteel senior was in his prime, Tompion was a mere stripling. The name of Fromanteel is synonymous with the classic age of British clockmaking, but it is not a British name—though this Fromanteel himself was born in Norwich, in 1607. His background is part of our social history, inevitably intertwined with our clockmaking history. In the early 1550s many Protestant families from Holland and northern Flanders fled to England to escape persecution, and it was a natural tendency, as well as a geographical one, that led them to settle in our 'low country'—East Anglia. It is possible that the Fromanteel family were originally from southern Flanders, the region which is now French-speaking Belgium; but even in that region they may have feared persecu-tion and joined in the migration. The forebears of Ahasuerus Fromanteel brought with them not only their skills in weaving cloth, but also their skills in things mechanical. The weavers tended to stay in East Anglia—the climatic conditions were suitable for wool—and the local inhabitants welcomed them; as a letter from the bailiff of Colchester stated, 'they are honest, civil, well-ordered—and godly'. One John Fromanteel is recorded in the list of officers of the Dutch Bay Company for Colchester in 1728, although beyond that date the name seems to disappear. John, who would have been the grandson of Ahasuerus senior, was listed as a 'White Haller', one of a chain of overseers or inspectors checking the quality of cloth production. (Incidentally, the 'Bay' in 'Dutch Bay Company' is a term used in clothmaking, not a place.)

The clockmaking immigrants, on the other hand, tended to gravitate towards London, the centre of the English clockmaking scene, such as it was in the early seventeenth century, and it was there that Ahasuerus senior journeyed to take up work as a journeyman clockmaker. It is believed that he had completed an apprenticeship under a Norwich turret-clockmaker and was, therefore, qualified to practice his art; in London, this meant being a member of one of the trade guilds. The nearest guild to that of clockmaking, which at the time of Fromanteel's arrival did not yet have its own, was that of the blacksmiths, and this he joined. That same year, 1631, the Clockmakers Company was founded, but membership of it was to prove a stumbling block to Fromanteel. The creation of the company was a defensive gesture by English clockmakers against foreign makers, notably the French (explaining the profusion of names like Goubert, Vallin and Vulliamy amongst the seventeenth and eighteenth century clockmakers), who were taking the lion's share of the trade. The irony was that the company soon became the bastion of the very people it had sought to exclude, especially during the reign of Charles I, who gathered about him pro-royalist clockmakers such as Edward East, and whose sympathies leaned towards Catholicism.

Fromanteel, being Protestant and also not a great believer in royalty, was immediately at odds with the company and especially with the then Master, Edward East. East had been made a freeman of the company almost at its inception and was Master twice, in 1645 and 1652. He lived to the age of eighty-three, so long that for a while it was thought that there were *two* Edward Easts! However, when Charles I was ousted by Cromwell in 1649, East could no longer justify refusing membership to a good parliamentarian and protestant. In 1656, Fromanteel, earlier made a brother of the company, was admitted as a freeman. That allowed him to advertise clocks under his own name and to take on a number of apprentices. Recently, however, it has come to light that some clockmakers never belonged to the Clockmakers Company, but belonged to other guilds engaged in like trades, such as the Woodworking Guild. They were allowed to advertise their 'wares', which could, of course, include a clock mechanism in a wooden case. Also, the court records are scattered with instances of clockmakers who were not 'free of the Guild', but had nevertheless taken on apprentices and advertised in their own names. Again, from a study of particular idiosyncracies, it is thought that some of the famous clockmakers advertised their clocks under the name of a freeman before they actually became one. However, membership and freedom of the Guild carried prestige and the chance of royal patronage, necessary to be able to produce the very expensive bracket clocks that are today's museum pieces.

While Fromanteel was engaged on the home front, he had despatched his son John to the old country, Holland, to work with Salomon Coster, who had translated Huygens' prototype (the turret clock) into a design for domestic clocks. Coster was, therefore, the expert in calculating pendulum lengths and gear ratios. John Fromanteel must have been quick to learn the new device because in 1658, after only one year's tuition from Coster, he was back in London and advertising them in *The Commonwealth Mercury*.

> There is lately a way found out for making of clocks that go exact and keep equaller time than any now made; without this Regulator (examined and proved before His Highness the Lord Protector by such Doctors whose knowledge and learning is without exception) and are not subject to alter by change of weather, as others are, and may be made to go a week, a month or a year with once winding up, as well as those that are wound up every day, and keep time as well, and is very excellent for all house clocks that go either with springs or weights; and also steeple clocks that are most subject to suffer by change of weather. Made by Ahasuerus Fromanteel, who made the first that were in England. You may have them at his house on the Bankside, in Mosses Alley, Southwark, and at the sign of the Mermaid in Lothbury, near Bartholomew Lane end, London.

This implies that Ahasuerus Fromanteel was making the pendulum clocks, but it seems to me that if the available information is correct there would not have been enough time between John's return and the publication of the article for him to have learned the technology of pendulum control thoroughly enough to make a clock for general sale. Perhaps John made the clock, to be advertised in his father's name, thereby solving two problems. The first was that John was not yet a freeman of the Clockmakers Company and therefore could not, by their rules, advertise his own clocks. He could, as we have seen, advertise anyway and risk prosecution, but with an important innovation in clock technology such as this he was unlikely to do that. The second problem was that the Fromanteels would be keen to exploit what was obviously a market advantage. The text of the advertisement is interesting, indicating that there were quite a few types of clocks in general use by this time, apart from lantern clocks (probably the ones referred to as 'those that are wound up every day').

The date of 1658 is significant in bracket-clock history, since recent evidence suggests that at least one type of clock made that year was a table clock with a pendulum—a transition stage from what was recognisable as a table clock to what is now recognisable as a bracket clock. The evidence is in the form of a clock that was in poor condition when found; it did however look as though it had originally fitted our definition of a bracket clock, being higher than it was wide (unlike the original table clocks, which did not have to make provision for a pendulum). The authenticity of the date inscribed on this clock (1658) is in some doubt—it does not look right, and it is too 'convenient' to find a clock that fits the date of the advertisement. Nevertheless, from the style of what remains, compared with complete examples of a later period, a date somewhere between 1658 and 1665 seems appropriate.

Despite this momentous event, horologically speaking, life had not yet finished with Fromanteel senior. In 1660, Charles II returned to the throne and it is likely therefore that the Clockmakers Company revived its earlier leanings. In the same year, Fromanteel's wife died and he returned to Colchester to marry the daughter of a merchant in the local Dutch community. In 1665, he again returned to Colchester to escape the ravages of the plague that was sweeping through London; shortly afterwards, his second wife died and Fromanteel was involved in a lawsuit with her father. By 1667, East was alive and well and still an influence within the pro-Royalist Clockmakers Company, whereas Fromanteel senior, aged sixty, was an old man. He returned to Holland —perhaps in disgust—joined later by his sons, John and Ahasuerus junior. (For a more detailed account of the Fromanteels and the life of this period, see *Country Clocks and their London Origins* by Brian Loomes, and *Clocks* magazine, volume 2 nos 11 and 12, volume 3 no 1.)

The first type of pendulum to appear was a simple 'bob' with a rigid steel arm. The end of the arm was formed into a screw thread, to which was screwed the bob, usually vase-shaped. All pendulum systems need some sort of fine adjustment because although the clockmaker may calculate the length of the pendulum, various other factors have to be considered, such as temperature variations and inaccuracy in the mechanical components. Screwing the bob up or down the pendulum arm effectively shortens or lengthens the pendulum, making the clock go faster or slower. As described in the previous section, it is the *length* of the pendulum that determines the time of swing, the bob being a device to help gravity to return the pendulum arm, and to act as a damper, or an aid to stability. As long as the weight is heavy enough to do this and yet is light enough to be driven by the clock movement, its actual weight is relatively unimportant.

Pendulums went through stages of development, but since these were linked to developments in escapements, or were introduced at a particular period of time, I have illustrated and explained them in later sections.

We now have the pendulum swinging merrily, but as Galileo found, we need to give it a push to keep it swinging. Also, whilst it *is* swinging we need to convert the pendulum movement (and the spring power) through a device which will allow the clock train to rotate—the escapement.

The Escapement

I have discussed briefly the early forms of escapement, and the first one that requires a more detailed explanation is the 'crown-wheel' type which appears in the earliest bracket clocks. A study of figure 5 (opposite) will explain why it is so called, the escapement wheel resembling a crown. When describing the operation of this escapement, this is some of the terminology used:

Wheel A gear wheel, usually of brass with the gear teeth formed around the outer rim.

Pinion A gear wheel, or cog wheel, usually of steel and in most cases a *driven* gear. Pinions used to be made from a length of pinion 'wire', thin steel rod already formed into the shape of the gear teeth. The gear teeth of a pinion are usually termed leaves (just to add to the confusion).

Arbor The shaft which carries a wheel or a pinion (often both). Today, the arbor is often formed from the pinion wire: once the position of the pinion is decided, the remainder of the pinion leaves are removed on a lathe, turning down the rod until a suitable arbor diameter is reached. A wheel may then be fitted on the arbor—usually as a 'drive' fit, by means of a collet—a heavy brass mounting bush.

Pivot The end of the arbor, turned down to a smaller diameter; the pivot then fits into the pivot hole in the end plates.

Pallet One of a pair of forks (of various design), which alternately engage the escapement wheel.

Sometimes the arbor is called the 'staff' and this term is itself the translation of 'verge'—a staff of office. Today, all escapements similar to that shown in figure 5 are called verge escapements, whereas that term should be reserved for the pre-bracket clock, pre-pendulum suspension of the foliot or balance-wheel type, in which the verge was a *vertical* shaft, and therefore resembled a staff of office held in the hand. It would be easier, too, if the term 'staff' was reserved for watches and the term 'arbor' for clocks. I have even seen an escapement listed as 'verge staff'— a kind of overkill. In this book, the component is called an arbor, not a verge, since it lies horizontally; although the primary component in earlier systems was termed a 'crown wheel', I shall reserve that term for the situation where it is situated in the plane in which a crown would be worn, ie with spikes uppermost! Therefore, enter the crown-wheel escapement.

In figure 5, the pendulum bob is attached to its vertical arm; this in turn is attached rigidly to the horizontal arbor. At one end of the arbor is

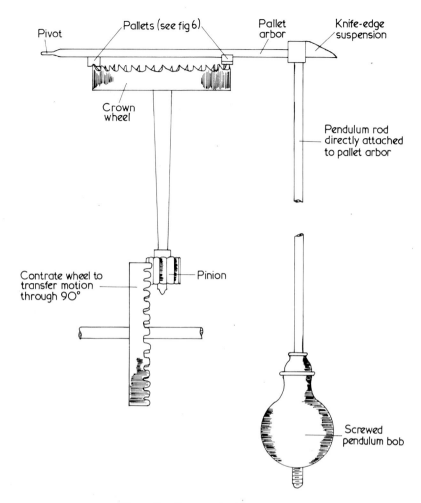

Figure 5   Crown-wheel escapement

a pivot, running in a pivot hole in the front plate of the movement, the other end being filed into a knife-edge, sitting in a V-block fitted to the back plate of the movement. In order to prevent the knife-edge jumping out of the V-block, an 'apron' is fitted to the end of the V-block, the apron having a small hole in which the point of the knife-edge sits. This apron was to become a decorative feature of the early bracket clocks, a simple, functional device being turned into a piece of artistry. Attached to the arbor are the two pallets; alternately, because of their configuration, these would engage and disengage the teeth of the escapement wheel, if the arbor was allowed to rock backwards and forwards. The escapement wheel is the final wheel in the clock train; it obtains its power from the spring and fusee.

If we imagine, for one moment, that the pallets are removed, it will be

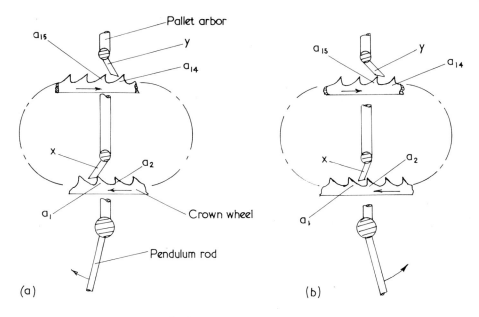

Figure 6   Crown-wheel escapement: progression of escapement wheel

apparent that, on winding up and releasing the spring, the whole clock train would start to revolve quite rapidly—even with a relatively slow-running fusee mechanism, the spring would have exhausted its strength in just a few minutes. It is prevented from running down by the action of the pallets. Figure 6 demonstrates how the crown wheel is allowed to 'escape', one tooth at a time, by the combined action of the force driving the escapement wheel, the swing of the pendulum and the positioning of the pallets.

Looking at figure 6a, as the pendulum nears the full extent of the (left) swing, pallet x lifts sufficiently to allow tooth a_1 on the crown wheel to escape. Any further escape is prevented by pallet y. This is so positioned on the arbor that as pallet x is lifting, y is lowering into the gap between teeth a_{14} and a_{15}, on the opposing side of the crown wheel. (I have transposed pallet y so that the two pallets can be seen relatively.) As tooth a_1 slips past pallet x, tooth a_{15} hits pallet y.

The pendulum reaches the extent of its swing and then starts to reverse (figure 6b). As it does so, pallet y is allowed by its chamfer to slide up the face of tooth a_{15} until, as the pendulum passes the vertical, it lifts completely clear of it; meanwhile pallet x has been lowered into the gap between teeth a_1 and a_2; as tooth a_{15} slips past the pallet, tooth a_2 comes up against pallet x.

The pendulum continues on its (right) swing, reaches its extent and then reverses direction. The cycle then starts over again. Of course if the pendulum was 'free-swinging' it would eventually come to rest; the spring power is used here, because the crown wheel is at all times being powered by the spring. For instance, as pallet x is lifting, due to the momentum of the pendulum, the pallet is helping the pendulum on its way—the tooth in contact with pallet x is *driving* the pallet.

Assuming for the moment that we place suitably sized wheels and pinions between the fusee and the escapement wheel, we now have a clock that will go. This part of the clock, logically, is called the 'going' side. But it does not strike the hours.

THE COUNTWHEEL STRIKING MECHANISM

The earliest clocks probably did not indicate the time with hands, and to sound the hours was their prime function. After all, the very word 'clock' is probably derived from the Latin *clocca*, a bell, or later the French *cloche*. Although the simplest clocks merely struck once on the hour, as a warning to the clock-minder, by the time of the bracket-clock era, from 1650 onwards, the striking mechanism would sound the hours.

The first such mechanism is known as the countwheel system, some-times referred to as the locking-plate system. A wheel 'counts' the hours from a series of slots cut in its rim at predetermined intervals. Figure 7 shows how this works. The countwheel detent normally rests in one of the slots. As the hour approaches, the lifting-piece is raised by the pin on the motion work and this, in turn, lifts both the countwheel detent and the hoopwheel detent, since these are fitted to a common arbor. At this stage, both detents are raised and the train will start to rotate, but as it does so a stop-pin fitted to the hoopwheel comes into contact with a projection on the lifting piece, stopping the train. The train is now at the 'warning' stage, under spring pressure and ready to run, but being prevented from doing so by the stop-pin. (It should be noted that, at this point, the notch in the hoopwheel has rotated away from the detent, so that if the detent were to fall, it would come to rest on the hoop and not in the notch.) The geometry of the lever is arranged so that as the minute hand reaches the hour, the lifting-piece falls away from the lifting-pin and, in falling, releases the stop-pin on the hoopwheel. The two detents fall with the lifting piece, but the hoopwheel detent cannot for the reason described above, enter its notch; since the two detents are rigidly connected the countwheel detent is also held clear of its notch.

The train is now free to run; the gearing is arranged so that for each revolution of the hoopwheel, the pinwheel causes the hammer to strike one blow. At each revolution, of course, the hoopwheel detent would be free to fall into its notch, but it can only do this if the countwheel detent has *also* reached a notch; the notches in the countwheel (sometimes

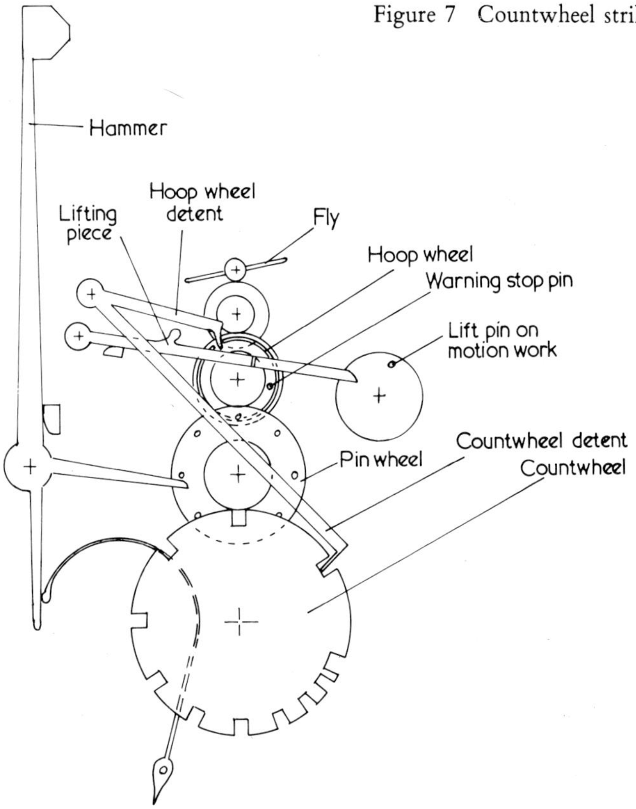

Figure 7   Countwheel strike mechanism

Hammer

Hoop wheel
detent

Lifting
piece

Fly

Hoop wheel
Warning stop pin

Lift pin on
motion work

Pin wheel

Countwheel detent
Countwheel

termed the locking-plate) are calibrated so that the correct number of hours are counted before the detent is allowed to fall into a notch. The strike is then locked off by the hoopwheel detent falling into its notch.

The 'warning' stage referred to earlier serves two purposes: it ensures that the detent cannot fall into the same countwheel notch twice—it must fall on the rim of the countwheel once the train is fully running (or, in the rack striking system described later, it ensures that the 'counting' device is able to operate reliably); and it ensures that the striking is at more or less constant speed—if the train had to accelerate from rest, it would have to overcome the complete inertia of the train before it attained a constant running speed. The warning device allows a short period of running to 'tighten' up that train, so that once the warning stop-pin is released the train can reach full speed in a very short time. The practical result (and aesthetic appeal) of this is that the hammer blows will be struck at regular intervals.

One problem that would arise is that the whole train, once the spring had overcome the inertia, might start to accelerate. To prevent this, all striking mechanisms are fitted with a 'fly' on the latter part of the train. The fly is easily recognisable—a rectangular plate, rotating on an arbor.

The principle is that of an air brake; the larger the plate area of the fly, the more it will act as a brake as it tries to cut through the air. The fly is not a solid fixture on its arbor, but is held in place by an integral spring-leaf. The reason for this is that, in rotating at fairly high speed, the fly builds up momentum: when the train comes to an abrupt halt, at the end of the striking period, a fixed fly could tear itself off its arbor, or break a few gear teeth with its stored-up energy. The spring fixing allows any such energy to be released, as the fly can continue to rotate on its arbor even though this is stationary. The fly is shown in figure 7.

The countwheel striking system was so successful and intrinsically reliable that French makers continued to use it until the end of the nineteenth century, and German and American companies producing the cheaper range of clocks used it into the early years of the twentieth century. Its cheap design was a strong enough advantage to outweigh its two main drawbacks. The system relied on the fact that the clock would be wound before the springs had run down completely. If the striking train ran down first—after, say, the clock had just struck 3—and the going train continued until the clock was rewound at, say, 6—the next hour recorded would be 7, but the next hour struck would be 4. With the early clocks, the only remedies for this drawback were either to raise the lifting-piece manually taking the countwheel through its sequence until it was synchronised once more, or, if the hour hand was a friction fit on its wheel arbor, to 'nudge' the hand anti-clockwise to coincide with the hour struck, and then advance the time again. This method is not to be recommended, and cannot be performed on the early bracket clocks, where the hour hand is screwed solidly to its arbor.

The other drawback, connected with the first, is the impossibility of fitting a usual type of 'strike/silent' device, since again when the clock is returned to the 'strike' mode the hour struck may not coincide with the hour recorded. Some countwheel clocks were made with a strike/silent lever, but it merely moved the hammer away from contact with the bell—the striking train was still allowed to operate.

THE ANCHOR OR RECOIL ESCAPEMENT

During the period 1650–70, while Fromanteel and others were improving the new pendulum system, two other significant events occurred. The first concerned the escapement mechanism. A characteristic of the crown-wheel escapement is that the pendulum has a fairly wide arc of swing, around 40–50°; also the light pendulum, directly attached to the pallet arbor was susceptible to variations in the driving power. The seventeenth-century clockmakers realised that the going

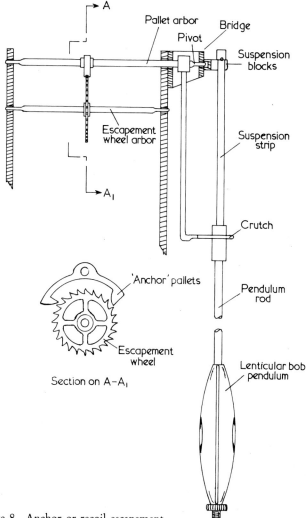

Figure 8   Anchor or recoil escapement

train and the escapement were controlling the pendulum, whereas the situation should be the reverse. The light pendulum was also unable to act as a damping device. In 1657 or thereabouts, Dr Robert Hooke (he of the 'Hooke's Law' used in engineering) claimed he had invented 'a device for continuing the motion of a pendulum'. It is not known for certain whether he applied this invention to a clock, but very shortly afterwards a William Clement brought forth such an escapement, fitted to a turret clock; the celebrated maker Joseph Knibb is also said to have used the device, though its first appearance is shrouded in uncertainty. By 1670 it was in general use and became known as the 'anchor' escapement, because of its shape. In horological circles, it is often known as the 'recoil' escapement, because of its action.

Figure 8 shows the general layout of the escapement. The pallets are no longer mere studs, fixed to the arbor; instead they are formed by the flukes of the anchor. The arbor does not sit in the unwieldly V-shaped slot, but now ends in a standard pivot, resting in a pivot-hole in the pendulum 'bridge'. An important feature is that the pendulum itself is not now rigidly attached to the pallet arbor. Instead it is attached to the pallet cock by means of two blocks; sandwiched between the blocks is a length of thin steel strip, by which means the pendulum rod is able to swing. A pin passes through the upper block, and rests in a notch filed into the bridge. To obtain a connection between the pendulum and the pallet arbor, a crutch, a fork-shaped component, is rigidly fixed to the arbor, and maintains a clearance fit around the lower suspension block. This system approaches the ideal of giving a free-swinging pendulum, and allows the use of a heavy pendulum bob, as well as a very small arc of swing, in the order of 5–8°.

The operation of this anchor or recoil escapement is shown in figure 9. As the pendulum swings to the left, with the escapement wheel rotating *clockwise*, it allows the tooth a_1 of the escapement wheel to slide along the impulse face of the pallet x, thus imparting an impulse to the pendulum, via the crutch; tooth a_1 then escapes past pallet x, but the escapement wheel is prevented from rotating further by tooth a_8 coming into contact with the curved face of pallet y. As the pendulum continues to swing to the left, this curved face results in the escapement wheel going into reverse, or recoiling, until the pendulum reaches its extent. As the pendulum then starts to swing right, the curved face of pallet y imparts impulse to the pendulum tooth a_8, then escapes past pallet y, and the cycle is repeated.

The recoil escapement was an immediate success, especially for use in turret and longcase clocks, but since bracket clocks were acceptable when fitted with the crown-wheel escapement, it was much later in the eighteenth century before their makers universally accepted the recoil escapement. The advantage of this escapement for the one-second or 'royal' pendulum in longcase clocks was that the small arc of swing allowed the pendulum to be put inside a case of aesthetically correct proportions: a crown-wheel escapement fitted with a 39 inch pendulum would require a case several feet wide!

THE RACK STRIKING SYSTEM

The second significant event was that of the invention, by the Rev Edward Barlow, of the 'rack' striking system in 1676. We have already seen that the countwheel strike had its problems, mainly that of

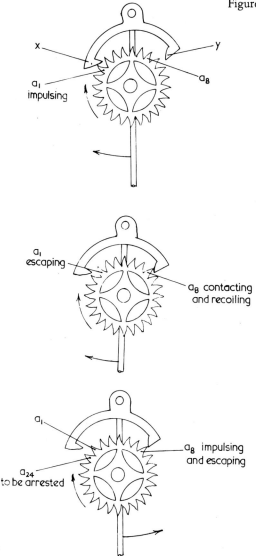

Figure 9 Anchor or recoil escapement: progression of escapement wheel

synchronisation; the rack system overcame this, since the hours recorded can never be out of phase with the hours struck. Figure 10 shows how the system works. The correct number of hours are counted by a plate fixed to the hour-hand arbor and rotating with it; this plate, called the 'snail' because its shape resembles a snail's shell, has twelve steps cut into it, each step corresponding to one hour. The rack lever, pivoted to the front plate (usually) of the clock movement, has twelve teeth. The teeth are 'gathered up' by a small projection, the gathering pallet, which rotates once for each blow struck on the hour bell; a rack hook prevents any movement of the rack whilst the gathering pallet is out of contact with it. A pin, at the end of the rack, comes into contact with the gathering pallet, locking the strike train, once all the teeth have been gathered. As the hour approaches, the rack hook is raised by the lifting-piece, allowing the rack tail, assisted by a leaf spring, to come into contact with the snail at the appropriate hour step.

A warning system is used, similar to that described in the countwheel system; here, as the strike train rotates, a stop-pin contacts a projection on the rack hook, stopping the train. This ensures that the train is tensioned, ready to run at full speed almost immediately, and that the rack tail is fully seated on the snail before the gathering pallet starts to rotate. As the hour arrives, the lifting-piece falls away from the pin on the motion work, causing the rack hook to fall away from the warning stop-pin. The train is now free to rotate, the gathering pallet picking up the correct number of rack teeth relative to the distance moved by the rack tail in falling to the snail.

There is a refinement in the rack tail to prevent damage should the strike train not operate (either by accident or design). It will be observed that the rack hook is lifted by the motion of the clock, by the *going* train; therefore the rack tail will be put into contact with the snail whether or not the strike train will then lift it clear. If, for instance, the strike-train spring has run down, the rack tail will slide along the circumference of the snail until the tail arrives at the step between 12 o'clock and 1 o'clock. At this point the snail, in attempting to rotate further, would

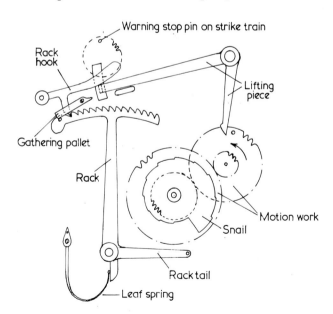

Figure 10 Rack striking mechanism

break either the rack tail or, worse, some of the teeth in the motion-work wheels. To prevent this, the majority of clocks have rack tails which are made from flexible strip metal, the snail having a chamfer filed along the vertical wall at the 12 o'clock to 1 o'clock step, so that the rack tail can ride over the step. Not all clocks are fitted with an effective override, especially if the tail has lost its resilience through age-hardening or has been 'repaired' by the substitution of a solid tail, so be warned! Unless you are absolutely sure which type of rack tail is fitted, make sure the strike side is wound up, and when advancing the hands let the striking sequence operate before you move on.

So, by 1670, all the major components have come together—the clock has a going train, driven by a fusee, and possibly a strike train also driven by a fusee (on English clocks); it has either the crown-wheel escapement or the recoil escapement. Succeeding chapters look at the bracket clock, not in isolation, but in the context of the social, economic and technological background, the market that was available and the factors that influenced the changes in design and manufacture.

4

THE ELEGANT AND THE ELITE, 1700–1750

The spring-driven bracket clock was in immediate demand, since from the outset it filled a gap in the nascent market for clocks in general. The turret or public clock was well established by 1650; it was better than nothing, even though it was notoriously inaccurate. As late as 1690 a correspondent complained to a newspaper that:

> I was in Covent Garden when the clock struck two, when I came to Somerset House by that clock it wanted a quarter to two, when I came to St. Clements it was half an hour past two, when I came to St. Dunstans it wanted a quarter of two, by Mr. Knib's Dyal in Fleet Street it was just two, when I came to Ludgate it was half an hour past one, when I came to Bow Church it wanted a quarter of two, by the Dyal near the Stocks Market it was a quarter past two and when I came to the Royal Exchange, it wanted a quarter of two: This I aver for a Truth, and desire to know how long I was walking from Covent Garden to the Royal Exchange.

This appeal from the heart shows the number of public clocks within a distance of about 1¾ miles. Only one of the clocks listed was directly connected with a clockmaker—'Knib' of Fleet Street. This was probably Joseph Knibb of Oxford, who worked in London until 1700 and was a prestigious maker of bracket clocks; we can assume that, with his reputation to uphold, Knibb's clock was correct in showing 2 pm. The walk would have taken about thirty minutes, so it seems that the Somerset House clock (1.45) and the Stock Market clock (2.15) were also correct. What is more important is the great discrepancy between these public clocks. The bracket clock of 1690 with either crown-wheel or recoil escapement was more accurate than the turret clocks appear to have been (even if the latter were being poorly maintained). And the story shows that the demand for accuracy existed. Yet as recently as 1923, one Ruth Belville would on a Monday morning set her Arnold chronometer by the clock at Greenwich Observatory and then visit some fifty clients in the locality to apprise them of the correct time (Felix Barker, *Historic Greenwich*).

From 1660 onwards wealthier people could buy one of the new longcase or hooded wall clocks (perhaps by Fromanteel) to solve the problem of domestic timekeeping. However, these were not portable, and if you wanted to know the time during the night you either had to stay awake long enough to hear the next hour struck by the longcase clock downstairs in the hall, or fuss about with flint and candle to read the time on your watch. This was the gap filled by the bracket clock, and from 1660 onwards it did not compete with the longcase but complemented it.

Since they were built for a relatively exclusive market and since ownership of them in itself conferred status, the early bracket clocks tended to be austere-looking. Such examples as survive from the period 1650–75 are plain in both looks and function. The case of such a clock presented a problem for two reasons; firstly there was no existing model to develop or improve, and secondly the clocks of this period were not purchased as 'matching co-ordinates' to go with the furniture, but were intended to be centrepieces. It was to be over a hundred years before clocks and furniture evolved a complementary pattern.

The first clock for detailed examination is one by Henry Jones (photograph 1). Jones was a noted clockmaker of the period, who was apprenticed in 1645, became Master of the fledgling Clockmakers Company in 1691 and died in 1695. This clock was made around 1675, is 16 inches high and 10 inches wide. The case design—figure 11 shows its general outline—is in the rather severe 'architectural' style popular in building design at that time, with the rare feature of a drawer beneath the dial, perhaps to hold the winding key. Overall it is of ebony veneer

Figure 11   Architectural-top case, c1675

1 (a) & (b) Front and rear views
of a clock by Henry Jones, c1675

on a solid timber frame, giving a durable, if plain, finish. The columns flanking the dial are in classical Corinthian style, with elaborate cast brass capitals. The brass 'swag' above the dial is also a classical building motif. The brass finials are urn-shaped and were probably made for this clock alone; the feet are turned from wood, as was usual in earlier clocks. The general style of the case is in fact similar in miniature to the aforementioned clock at St Dunstan's, which was built in 1671. One feature yet to be developed was a handle, though, without a strike/silent device, this clock would be little use in the bedroom at night.

The dial is a single sheet of cast brass, hammered flat, with a separate chapter ring of silvered brass pinned to it. The corners of the dial are filled by cast brass spandrels, otherwise known as 'corner pieces'. The spandrels here are typical of the period, being of cupid's-head design, with an overall simplicity of form. The centre of the dial is matted (sometimes termed frosted) by a hand tool. The hands are steel and non-matching. The minute hand has decorative scrolls close to its root, a straight pointer forming two-thirds of its length. The hour hand is very typical of the period, decorated towards the tip with a fairly plain root section. Both hands have been cut and filed by hand (figure 12).

The movement is well engineered, though devoid of decoration, and has a crown-wheel escapement with a bob pendulum; as we have seen, although the recoil escapement was established by this time, clockmakers saw no reason to abandon the crown wheel. The strike mechanism is of the countwheel type—the rack striking system had yet to be invented. Consequently there is no strike/silent device, as discussed in chapter 3.

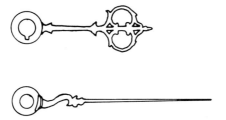

Figure 12   Hand styles, c1675

THE MARKET FOR THE BRACKET CLOCK

Once the buying public had accepted the bracket clock its market increased rapidly. We are not, however, dealing with 'mass markets' in today's terms, and it is interesting to surmise the possible market available at any one time. This is particularly important in the nineteenth century, when the population of the United Kingdom rose rapidly; it is reasonably easy to demonstrate that the English clockmaker could never satisfy the market at any one time and that once the population had risen to a number giving a total market justifying mass-production methods, the competition must become fierce.

How could we estimate how many people not only bought clocks but were in the market for clocks? One way (as good as any) is to use a calculation called the Pareto Rule, sometimes known as the 80–20 Rule, one of those natural laws that seem to be adaptable to various situations. For instance, the Rule says that 20 per cent of the population own 80 per cent of the wealth of the nation. The engineering industry employs the rule when stock control is necessary: the top 20 per cent of components, in value terms, account for 80 per cent of the total stock—control those items and the rest will look after themselves. This ratio applies to modern society, but as we go back in time a correction factor is needed. For the year 1700, we should probably say that 5 per cent of the population owned 95 per cent of the nation's total wealth, and of that 5 per cent, assuming the usual ratios, 48 per cent would have been male and 52 per cent female. This factor may not be important in today's 'equal' society, but in any period before 1900 only the male in the household would buy a clock. A further factor is that not all of the males would be of appropriate age—some 25 per cent would be too young and some 25 per cent be old enough not to bother with those new-fangled contraptions. This leaves us with a sum total of potential clock buyers in, say, 1700 of:

n (population) × 0.05 (wealthy) × 0.48 (male) × 0.5 (right age)
= n × 0.012 or 1.2 per cent of the population.

So far, so good, as a rough estimate—but not everyone will buy a new clock every year! To keep the calculation manageable, it would be reasonable to assume that in any one year only the increase in population would be potential buyers. That assumes that someone who bought a clock in 1700 would still have it at the time he died, but is this not realistic? Many, many clocks have passed through generations of the same family.

Population of the United Kingdom (millions)

1650	5.4 (estimate)	1851	22.2
1700	6.5 (estimate)	1861	24.5
1750	8.2 (estimate)	1871	27.4
1801	10.5	1881	31.0
1811	13.3	1891	34.2
1821	15.4 (estimate)	1901	38.2
1831	17.8	1911	42.0
1841	20.1	1921	44.0
		1931	46.0

The table gives us a figure of, for 1650, 5.4m × 0.012 = 64,800.

Of course some of these 65,000 people would already own a lantern clock or a watch by the time the bracket became popular, but the figures, however inaccurate, show that the clockmakers could not possibly supply the potential market. By 1700 the market would have increased by 13,000, so that they could not even supply the *increase*, let alone every previously existing potential buyer. This, of course, is a nice position to be in: however expensive you make your clock, there will almost always be someone wanting to buy it.

THE ARRIVAL OF ELABORATION

Though this situation was not the sole reason, from 1675 onwards the bracket clock moved away from its early severe lines, developing decorative and expensive features. The plain architectural top gave way to the 'basket' shape, fashioned in wood or brass (or silver in the most expensive clocks), and taking on several variations over the next few years, until its demise in about 1710. The basic shapes are shown in figure 13. These basket tops invariably terminate in a substantial, and therefore functional, handle, usually of cast brass, and more brasswork appears everywhere. The sides of the cases had panels of brass castings (later developing into a fretwork pattern) and the feet were often of brass, with brass castings to the front door.

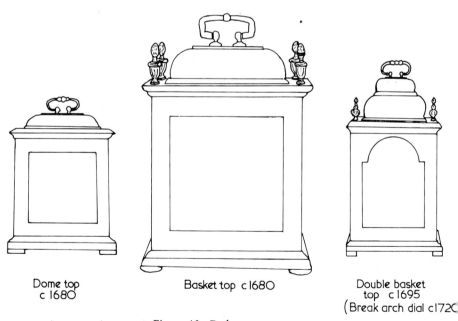

Dome top
c 1680

Basket top c 1680

Double basket
top c 1695
(Break arch dial c1720

Figure 13 Basket tops

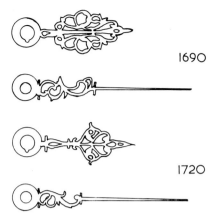

1690

1720

Figure 14   More elaborate hand styles

The dial remained in essence like that of earlier clocks, but the hands became generally more elaborate, already moving towards a standard pattern that would exist for almost one hundred years; the minute hand was the same straight pointer with a scrolled root, the hour hand now beginning to have its decorative work closer to the root (figure 14). Like the architectural top, the basket top and its variants had a relatively short lifespan; it was to succumb to a case design that had been evolved around 1685 and that would, with its variants, dominate for the next hundred years or so. This was the 'bell-top' style, shown in figure 15, named for

Bell top c1740

Inverted bell
top c1715

Figure 15   The true bell-shaped top came after the inverted bell-top

its resemblance to the cross-section of a bell. In fact, the true bell-shaped top did not arrive until about 1740, the earlier design being the 'inverted' bell-top. One of the best illustrations of this style is the bracket clock by Daniel Quare, dating from about 1690, shown in photograph 2. Quare, a contemporary of Tompion, was a noted clockmaker, with some fine bracket and longcase clocks to his credit. He was born in 1649, made free of the Clockmakers Company in 1671, was the Master of the Company in 1708 and died in 1724.

The case design of this clock is exuberance personified! The striking feature is the Chinese lacquerwork, taking the place of the more usual ebony veneer and brass decoration. Lacquerwork (which was revived in the Edwardian era) was a popular fashion during the late seventeenth century, stemming mainly from the activities of the English and Dutch East India Companies. If nothing else it was a sign of wealth to own a clock such as this, made obviously without much regard to costs. This clock appears to have been fashioned in 'genuine' lacquer, having an original 1690 finish and not a later, and much poorer, renovation. True lacquer uses the lac, or resin, of an insect, and was very rarely used in Europe, but the Dutch and English lacquerers developed a satisfactory substitute, using gesso coatings with a base colour. On this was drawn the oriental figure work, to which a tacky shellac was applied; upon this, silver and gold powders were built up, giving a slightly three-dimensional effect. This clock has the inverted bell-top case, the lower half of the top being bell-shaped but the top half resembling a bell shape turned inside out. The top is surmounted by a brass carrying handle, and the finials and feet are in brass.

As on the Jones clock, the dial is of one-piece cast brass, with cupid's-head spandrels, and the chapter ring is of silvered brass. The hands are typical of this period, the minute hand decorated close to the root, and the hour hand elaborately worked; they are filed from steel and would originally have been blued by heating in a bed of sand, followed by oil quenching. The dial has the additional feature of calendar work, with the date showing through a cut-out below the numeral XII. The use of calendar work was well established by this date, although its design caused problems then—as now. The calendar, of course, moves only once in twenty-four hours and, ideally, should move only as the actual date changes; if it is geared directly to the clock mechanism it will be moving, albeit slowly, all the time. The clockmakers solved this problem by having a 1:2 ratio wheel, driven from the hour wheel, thus allowing one revolution in twenty-four hours. This wheel is not geared to the calendar ring, but is fitted with an extended pin which contacts the serrations on the calendar ring for about two hours only during the

2   Clock by Daniel Quare, c1700

3   Rear of Daniel Quare clock

twenty-four hours; by convenient setting, these two hours may be at dead of night! The calendar ring itself rests within three grooved idler wheels, the idea being that it is then free-running; but of the whole clock mechanism this has been the part that gives the most trouble. It is liable to seizing-up, due to wear on the idler wheels or dirt inside the case, and many old bracket clocks have at some time had the calendar work removed to effect a cheap 'repair' in order to get the clock to go again.

A significant point on the dial has deliberately been left to the last. The clock appears to be a simple timepiece, since there is only one winding-hole, but this is not so. A study of the movement, shown in photograph 3, reveals the presence of two bells, with their hammers, sitting above the movement; to the right of the movement is a cord, stretched between the movement and the side of the case. The striking mechanism, to give it its correct definition, is 'pull-repeat, quarter chiming on two bells'. This chiming sequence (which is discussed, with others, in a later chapter) gives an indication of the time, to the nearest quarter of an hour. The bells are matched in harmonic thirds or fifths so that they give a 'ting-tang' sound, with one ting-tang for each quarter hour. The hour is sounded on the deeper-toned bell, the hour struck being the *last* hour passed. As an example, if the clock was indicating 3.45 when the cord was pulled, the sequence would be:

ting-tang, ting-tang, ting-tang (3 quarters); tang, tang, tang (past 3 o'clock).

The mechanism must use the rack-and-snail method of counting the hours, the snail revolving with the movement but being brought into use when the cord is pulled. A further refinement is added to the snail, a device known as a star-wheel. Here the snail is not mounted on the hour-hand arbor, as it would be in a 'standard' clock, but is on a separate arbor, attached to the star-wheel and independent of the clock train. Within a few minutes of the hour, a pin mounted on the hour wheel operates a 'flirt', causing the star-wheel and snail to rotate to correspond with the oncoming hour. The snail will then be locked in this position until a few minutes before the next hour.

To illustrate the usefulness of this device, imagine the scene where a wealthy merchant of the late seventeenth century is preparing for bed. He takes his bracket clock from the hall or drawing-room, locks the pendulum on to its latch and carries the clock upstairs. He places it so that he can reach the pull-repeat cord whilst in bed, sets the clock in motion and goes off to sleep. (If he is *really* wealthy, he may have a clock by Master Tompion that has a pull-repeat cord on each side of the case.) Let us say he wakes up in the early hours and decides that if it is 6 o'clock he will rise, otherwise he will go back to sleep. If the time happened to be 5.40 when he pulled the cord, a 'standard' striking clock without the star-wheel device would probably strike 6; moreover, it would still strike 6 when the actual time was, say, 6.25. The reason for this is that the snail has definite steps, each step with a fairly wide 'land' to allow for slight inaccuracies in the fall of the rack. Having a ting-tang mechanism solves the problem of the quarter-hours, but to get round the latitude in the hours, the star-wheel is necessary. If it is 5.40, the star-wheel and snail will still be locked into the 5 o'clock position and our merchant would hear 2 ting-tangs and 5 blows, and therefore know that the time was after 5.30 but before 5.45.

The strike train in the clock by Daniel Quare is not driven by any normal means; it would be possible to link it in with the single fusee and spring of the going train, but that would demand a spring of sufficient strength to supply both trains for a period of eight days, as well as the 'random' operation of the pull-repeat. If our merchant wanted to show off his prize possession to his friends by repeatedly operating the strike train, the spring would very soon run down. So the strike train in the Quare clock is separated from the going train, but is not wound in the normal manner with a key; instead, pulling on the cord coils a spring in a barrel: as soon as the cord is released, the spring uncoils, driving the strike train. I have not been able to examine this clock in detail, but the evidence for the separate spring barrel (apart from it being logical) is the presence of a large-diameter arbor, showing through the back plate in the centre of the upper-right scroll circle.

The back plate is profusely engraved, as one would expect in a clock of this quality and period. The unusual feature of the movement is that it has a balance-wheel escapement, where one would expect to find a crown-wheel escapement and bob pendulum. (The pointer is for slow/fast adjustment, similar to the system used in modern watches and clocks.) It seems that Quare fitted a balance wheel to facilitate carrying the clock about since of course a balance wheel is impervious to changes in direction or angle; the disadvantage would be that this system was probably not as accurate as a pendulum system, certainly not until well into the eighteenth century.

As we move into the eighteenth century, bracket clocks begin to assume set patterns of design. The cases of the middle-of-the-market clocks were still in ebony veneer, usually on an English oak carcase, the case tops being variations on the basic inverted bell or basket styles, all with an increasing tendency to simplicity of line and form that allowed a wide, flat area above; this area made a substantial carrying handle a part of the aesthetic balance of the case, rather than looking like an addition.

The movement would be either crown-wheel or recoil escapement, the former being more suited to a portable clock, since the pallet clearances and the wide swing of the pendulum could better tolerate being tipped out of alignment—useful on tables standing on uneven early eighteenth-century floors! The recoil escapement, with its smaller pallet clearances and narrow arc of pendulum swing, was—and is—more susceptible to alignment errors. (This is especially true in the German clocks of the late nineteenth-early twentieth century, which are sometimes super-critical of non-level surfaces.) This was, perhaps, the main reason for the survival of the crown-wheel escapement, since its timekeeping qualities do not match those of the recoil.

Bracket-clock dials, in general, remained much the same over the first twenty years of the eighteenth century, as a square plate of brass, with a separate, silvered chapter ring and cast brass spandrels. The spandrels, from 1700 onwards, became much fussier, with more scrollwork and less detail, although the cherub's-head spandrel was still popular. The hands, also, were losing their elaborate detail and there is evidence that even by 1710 hands and spandrels were being batch-produced; provincial bracket clocks of this period turn up with these components made to the same design, even though the clockmakers were geographically many miles apart. This is not to say that the clocks were deteriorating; more to the point, the makers were probably looking to the new market—the middle class—that was beginning to develop. People with money could still purchase in, say, 1710 a clock by Fromanteel jnr, Tompion, Quare, or Tompion's partner George Graham; if the price was right, the clock could incorporate the very best of technology and art.

GEORGE GRAHAM

George Graham was born in Cumbria, but apprenticed in London, and it was on becoming a freeman of the Clockmakers Company in 1695 that he went into partnership with Tompion—in fact he did more than that, he married Tompion's niece. Many of his contemporaries waged feuds, both privately and publicly, with each other, but Graham, known as 'Honest George' because of his fair dealings, remained aloof; during Tompion's life, his work and ambitions were overshadowed by the charisma of his partner. Certainly the bracket clocks they produced bear remarkable similarities, even down to the twin pull-repeat mechanisms, said to have been introduced by Tompion. I have yet to be convinced that Tompion deserves the high esteem that has been accorded to him down the years; some of his clocks that nowadays sell for astronomical sums may show craftsmanship, but they do not exhibit an artist's eye for

4 & 5   Front and rear views of a clock by George Graham, c1720

aesthetic balance. The values of such clocks would fall to realistic levels if one day it was proved that they were, in fact, made by Graham, or one of Tompion's better apprentices.

A clock by Graham, one representative of the period 1715–20, is shown in photographs 4 and 5. The case is in ebony veneer on a hardwood carcase and, typical of Graham's work, is kept fairly plain and simple. There is brass ornamentation round both the real door-lock and the false door-lock (done to preserve symmetry), and the carrying handle and 'ogee' feet are brass; otherwise there is no decoration. The top is of the inverted bell form, very popular during this period, and the case sides contain glass panels through which the movement can be seen. The clock stands 16 inches high, is 9½ inches wide and 5½ inches deep.

The dial is brass, still square in outline at this time, with a silvered-brass chapter ring. The spandrels are retained to fill in the dial corners; they are still in the cherub's-head design but its clarity is diminishing. The dial centre is nicely matted and contains the calendar aperture and the 'mock-pendulum' aperture, which became very popular from about 1695 and remained a feature until the end of the eighteenth century. It was only effective as a visual display on a crown-wheel escapement movement, with its wide angle of pendulum swing, the mock pendulum-bob being a disc attached to a dog-leg arm, connected to the pallet arbor. Apart from providing an attractive display, it also indicated to the owner that the clock was going again after being transported.

Up to this period, the strike/silent lever had been sited through a small, horizontal slit above the numeral XII, but on this clock it assumes more importance as an intrinsic part of the dial, a feature which was to develop over the next few years. Here it is a pointer moving through 180° between the letters S (for strike) and N (for not strike). As in the earlier form, the pointer operated to displace the lifting-piece of the strike train, so that the pin would not lift it on the approach of the hour.

The dial is balanced by the addition of a second subsidiary dial on the left, having a pointer rotating on a graduated dial. These graduations are intended for decoration only, the purpose of the device being to allow adjustment of the pendulum length without the need to delve into the back of the clock. The view of the movement in photograph 5 shows how it works. At the top right-hand side of the movement, is a curved rack arm, running behind a plate. Inside the plate is a wheel attached to the dial pointer; when the pointer is rotated, the wheel drives the rack up or down (the device is usually called 'up-and-down work'), and since the pendulum suspension strip is affixed to this arm, the length of the pendulum can be varied. The effective length starts at the 'chops', just below the point where the strip is fixed to the arm.

The other significant feature of the movement is the twin pull-repeat device, easily recognisable as the work of the Tompion/Graham partnership. The movement drive is by spring and fusee, on both the going and striking train, and is as one would expect extremely well engineered. An unusual feature is that, apart from the well-shaped pillars and the decorative tails to the fixing brackets, the movement is quite plain. On a clock of this quality and period, one would expect profuse engraving, not necessarily the work of the maker but subcontracted to jobbing engravers. This movement is devoid of such frills except for the signature and is typical of Graham's work. One often finds such simple lines on the work of the Quaker clockmakers, such as the Upjohns of Exeter, their faith being reflected in the absence of unnecessary additions in all branches of their work. It has not been proved that George Graham was a Quaker, but several members of his family were, including his father; and his work and life seem to run in parallel with the Quaker philosophy of 'peace with profit'. After Tompion's death in 1713, the following announcement appeared in the *London Gazette*:

> George Graham, nephew of the late Mr Thomas Tompion, who lived with him upwards of seventeen years, and managed his trade for several years past, whose name was joined with Mr. Tompion for some time before his death, and to whom he left all his stock and work, finished and unfinished, continues to carry on the said trade at the late Dwelling House of the said Mr Tompion, at the sign of the Dial and Three Crowns, at the corner of Water Lane, in Fleet Street, London, where all persons may be accommodated as formerly.

Graham's technology seemed to blossom after Tompion's death and he turned his attention to new fields of horology, but his best-known contribution to bracket-clock development was the 'dead-beat' escapement, shown in figure 16. The recoil escapement had been reasonably successful for forty-five years, but it had the inherent disadvantage of 'recoiling' the escape wheel, which had a consequent effect, however slight, on the action of the pendulum. In the dead-beat escapement, invented in 1715, the anchor swings in an arc which passes through the centre-line of the escapement-wheel arbor, and the angles of the wheel teeth and pallet entrance face are such that the pallet slides down the face of the tooth without driving the tooth in reverse. Only when the pendulum swings back towards the vertical is an impulse given by the tip angle of the pallet. Whereas the earlier form remained in driving contact with the pendulum for most of its swing, the dead-beat design tried to simulate the earliest form of free-swinging pendulum, giving it a nudge as it passed the centre line, to keep it swinging, but otherwise allowing it to free-swing in the remainder (or supplement) of

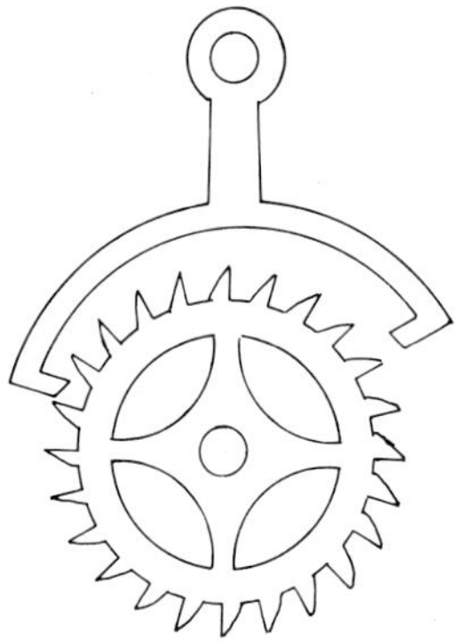

Figure 16 Graham's dead-beat escapement, invented in 1715

its arc. The dead-beat escapement improved the timekeeping of bracket clocks, but because of its action it did suffer from lubrication problems and could quite easily be rendered ineffective by dirt on the pallets.

Graham's original design, with almost infinitesimal pallet drop and vertical faces to the backs of the escape-wheel teeth, was a temperamental escapement—when working it worked very well, but it was not reliable when used in domestic clocks. In practice, clockmakers modified the design, attempting to get near to the action of the Graham form while maintaining reliability. The escapement shown in figure 16 (taken from a bracket clock) is one of these variations. It has greater pallet drop and a different tooth from Graham's original; it would give a more vigorous pendulum movement, but with a small amount of recoil.

The modified forms were used successfully on the better-quality clocks, especially the type known as 'mantel regulators', the bracket-clock equivalent of the longcase regulators, and continue to be used today in high-quality reproductions of the wall-mounted regulator. The action of the dead-beat escapement may be observed by looking at one of the 'visible-escapement' French clocks of the later nineteenth century. This is a variation of the dead-beat escapement, with pallets of hardened steel or gemstones; not a true dead-beat but with a similar action.

Between the years 1720 and 1725, the clock dial, and consequently the case, underwent a radical change, with the introduction of the 'break-arch' dial (figure 17). As the name implies, it is not the full width of the dial, from which it is stepped in to form a smaller arc. This change could have followed the furniture design of the time, since there are corner cupboards and bookcases from the George I and George II period with this feature. Which came first, the clock or the furniture, is debatable (it depends on where your loyalties lie, I suspect), but certainly, the longcase clocks display the same break-arch dial from about 1725.

The break-arch opened up both functional and decorative possibilities. It allowed the strike/silent lever to be raised into the arch, where it was easier to operate, and easier to see at a glance the state of the strike train.

On other clocks, of a slightly inferior quality, we find the break-arch dial employed to house a cartouche bearing the maker's name; this was an especially useful ploy for the provincial makers, who could buy a London movement complete with a dial in the latest fashion. If the customer wanted an expensive clock, the strike/silent mechanism could be fitted into (or bought with) a two-train movement; for a cheaper clock, the strike/silent could be fitted into the dial in the earlier style (above the numeral XII), or not fitted at all—in which case the strike could not be silenced; or the clock could be a timepiece only, or one that repeated at will using a subsidiary, non-fusee spring barrel, in the manner of the Quare clock, photograph 2.

Figure 17   Break-arch dial and case, c1720

I am not implying that every clock of this style had a bought-in London movement—merely that it *could* have had. The movement must be examined to judge whether it was an individual and unique piece of work. One indication is that a bought-in movement made to incorporate a strike/silent device would probably have an extended arbor, holding the strike-train lifting-piece; if this is not being used for its purpose, it should be quite noticeable. Sometimes, though rarely in bracket clocks, the break-arch would have, from 1750 onwards, a phases-of-the-moon indicator. In a bracket clock this device would be for decoration only, since the people who could afford to buy the clock would not be interested in the exact state of the moon, beyond looking out of their window; for country people, the state of the moon was often an integral part of their daily (and dusky) lives, so that the device was more usually incorporated into the one and only clock they would have, the family longcase.

A word of warning may be appropriate here. When considering the purchase of a bracket clock with a break-arch dial, check whether the dial and the arch are formed of a single sheet of brass. If they are not, it does not necessarily mean that the clock is a fake, as some movement makers could have had stocks of square dials and converted them to arch dials when the fashion took hold. A marriage such as this, done by a craftsman, will be impossible to detect from the front of the dial, the proof being that the clock and case have no surplus or extraneous holes; therefore the movement was fitted to an original case. Clock cases may of course deteriorate from damage or natural causes, and a repairer or dealer may then have a nice square-dial movement looking for a case. If a suitable case happens along, but is of the break-arch style, it is a simple matter to tack an arch on to the movement. The marriage should be fairly easy to spot. Other means of faking are discussed in the chapter on collecting bracket clocks.

Two clocks that illustrate the break-arch style are shown in photographs 6 and 7. The earlier one, dating from about 1725, is by James Markwick of London, who was a Master of the Clockmakers Company in 1720 and died in 1730. This was a clock for the upper end of the market, with fine lacquering to the inverted bell-top case. The dial is of the best quality, with cherub's-head spandrels (the last time we shall see this design in general use) and full cherub figures in the break-arch. Here the break-arch has been used for the signature, so the strike/silent is relegated to the earlier position. Markwick supplied both domestic and overseas markets, especially the Middle and Far East, and it is likely that some of his best lacquer cases were sent out to the Far East to have the finish applied. The movement of the clock has a crown-wheel escapement and is extremely well engineered. The trains are each supplied by fusee and spring.

In contrast, the clock by John Rayment of Huntingdon, made in about 1760, is for the middle of the market. It is veneered in ebony, still by 1760 a popular fashion, on a case of inverted bell-top design; although the true bell-top styles had been introduced by about 1740, the inverted style remained until the 1760s. The glass panels in the sides of the case were a continuing feature through the eighteenth century; however, the glass inserts filling in the arch of the case are replacements, since there is only the case carcase behind them; originally there would have been a wood or brass fretwork design here, similar to that of the Markwick case. The spandrels exhibit the changes that occurred towards the middle

6   James Markwick clock, c1730

7 (a) & (b) Front and rear views of a clock by John Rayment, c1760

of the eighteenth century. They are by now much less well-defined castings, probably mass-produced with a fussy rococo design; in this price range, they were to remain in this style until the demise of the square dial. The movement is a timepiece only but as the rear view illustrates, there is a subsidiary pull-repeat mechanism, chiming on two bells. The escapement is of the crown-wheel type.

As the second quarter of the eighteenth century drew to a close, England was enjoying a period of relative prosperity, under the kingship of George II. A great deal of exploration was already in the past, the empire was being built and major trade routes had been established. The population could enjoy the spices of the east, and clocks and furniture veneered in exotic woods with exotic names—amboyna, kingwood, coromandel, birds'-eye maple, amongst others; indeed, English hardwoods such as walnut and pearwood were rapidly becoming scarce and supplies would only recover once the fashion for foreign woods had decreased the demand. The most popular of these imported timbers proved to be mahogany, introduced into England in about 1740. This was not the mahogany we buy today for our do-it-yourself projects—a mere shadow of the quality of the eighteenth century product; it was a very hard wood from the West Indies and surrounding areas, known by various names including 'Cuban', 'Spanish' and 'Jamaican'. It is a well-figured wood, much darker than we now expect mahogany to be, with a silky-smooth texture giving an excellent polished finish. At first it was used as a carcase on which to veneer other woods, but it quickly came into its own as an economical finish; the main advantage in using it for both veneer and carcase was that there was less likelihood of the veneer splitting, or separating from the carcase, since the coefficient of expansion (and contraction) was the same for both.

DUTCH AND FRENCH COMPETITION

The population had increased to around 8 million by 1750, which by our rough calculation would result in about 20,000 more customers for bracket clocks than there were in 1700, these to be added to the numbers of customers still waiting in the queue for a clock! The clockmakers had the domestic market almost to themselves, as well as a stake in several overseas markets. The only serious competition, and that in no way devastating, came from France and Holland. The Dutch clockmakers, as we have seen, were one step ahead of the English in the application of the pendulum, and throughout the years 1660–1750 there was cross-fertilisation and slight competition between the two nations. The Dutch had no tradition in bracket-clock design and the examples appearing in the early eighteenth century could easily be mistaken for English makes, especially if the maker *was* English, or had an English-sounding name—an example is Roger Dunster of Amsterdam. One feature that often points to a Dutch design is the addition of an alarm-setting disc in the centre of the dial. This was unusual in an English clock (although not unique), but in Holland it had been traditional for wall clocks to have alarm devices many years before the introduction of the bracket clock.

In 1704 the Master of the Clockmakers Company complained that 'certain persons at Amsterdam were in the habit of putting the names of Tompion, Windmills, Quare and other well-known London makers on their works and selling them as English'. Should the reader have a Tompion clock stashed away in a bank vault, check it now! If it is a 30-hour movement (a common feature of Dutch bracket clocks), then I don't want to worry you—but. . . . . This trading in makers' names was not confined to England and Holland, nor was it confined to bracket clocks—watches too had spurious signatures engraved. English makers exporting to the Iberian peninsula and the East often made subtle changes to their names and engraved meaningless 'foreign' symbols on their

Figure 18 Boulle inlaid 'waisted' case
with matching bracket—French, c1780

clocks. English clockmakers at the end of the nineteenth century would
raise an outcry at the number of imported clocks made in English style,
but their forebears had done just the same in reverse while the trade was
good in the eighteenth century—one English clockmaker exported so
much to Spain that he was nicknamed Diego Evans.

Holland was a minor threat; France potentially posed a greater danger
—though at first the French clock designs were a little too much for
English taste; they made a bigger impact during the later eighteenth and
early nineteenth century, when English furniture makers gave vent to an
exuberance of design. French style of the seventeenth and early
eighteenth centuries was the 'baroque', of which the 'rococo' was a
development. Just as in England, clock manufacture and new designs
blossomed under royal patronage. Louis XIV bought French clocks for
the Palace at Versailles and later for other establishments. The most
notable designer of the late seventeenth-century period was Andre
Charles Boulle (1642–1732), who produced magnificent designs using
inlays and marquetry in tortoiseshell, brass, silver, mother-of-pearl and
other exotic materials. As far as clocks were concerned, the mechanism
took second place to the case design, a tendency that was continued all
through the eighteenth century and that perhaps alienated the English
clock-buying public during this period.

Most of the earlier clocks of the Boulle era were bracket clocks, but
they were mounted on a floor pedestal, a design that developed naturally
into a longcase-style clock. Some, however, were designed specifically as

wall-mounted bracket clocks. During the reign of Louis XV, from 1723 onwards, a more classical style evolved, using simpler lines, and it was during this period that the popular 'waisted' bracket clock appeared (figure 18). During the eighteenth and nineteenth centuries this clock, unlike English designs, was almost always made with a matching bracket, which it only lost in the transition from bracket to mantel clock in the later nineteenth century.

Some of these clocks really are magnificent specimens, standing 3 feet tall without the bracket (which would add at least another 2 feet), veneered in tortoiseshell or animal horn, sometimes lacquered, the most expensive ones being cast in bronze. The sheer size is daunting; a large room or hall is needed to set them off, which may be one reason why the number imported was relatively small. As the years went on, the size was reduced, bringing them into competition with the English clocks.

The movements of these clocks displayed nothing like the engineering skill of the English makers, but as shown in the chapter on spring drives French movements were to present a serious challenge to the English makers by the end of the eighteenth century. Initially, they were simple, rectangular plate types, devoid of decoration, but the significant feature was the absence of a fusee. As said earlier, the French rarely used the fusee system, preferring instead to use a long, weak spring to obtain a reasonable degree of 'smoothing' of the varying spring force. The design, of course, resulted in a much smaller mechanism than the one fitted to English clocks, a feature which was to be important in the years to come.

5

A CONFUSION OF STYLES, 1750–1800

As we open the curtain on this era in the development of the bracket clock, the most famous names are missing. The clockmaking members of the families Fromanteel, East, Tompion, Quare, Knibb and Graham were all dead. But their work and their pioneering designs remained, to be developed by the makers following them.

In the year 1750, the best-known maker was John Harrison. He invented the 'grasshopper' escapement and helped to solve the problem of finding the longitude whilst at sea. The grasshopper escapement, however, is more commonly found in regulator and turret clocks, so details belong to more general books on horology.

A device of Harrison's that was used in bracket clocks was the grid-iron pendulum rod. He, like others before him, had discovered that clock pendulums, being fairly large components, were affected by changes in temperature; one solution was to use a rod of high-density wood, such as ebony or lignum vitae, but even this was susceptible to temperature change. George Graham (who else?) had produced one answer in 1726, with his introduction of the mercury pendulum. Both these types of compensating pendulum were used in top-quality bracket clocks, so it is more convenient to discuss them at this juncture. The two are shown in figure 19. In the mercury pendulum, Graham did away with the pendulum-bob, substituting a glass jar containing a quantity of mercury; obtaining the correct proportions of mercury height to pendulum length gave the equivalent of a normal pendulum length. Imagine a rise in ambient temperature. The metal rod holding the jar of mercury will heat up and, in doing so, will expand (or increase in length); the mercury will also expand, the only expansion possible being to rise in level, so that, in theory, the lowering of the pendulum mass by expansion of the rod is counteracted by the raising of the *effective* mass, due to the rise in mercury level. In a perfectly designed system the two movements cancel each other out, the effective pendulum length remaining the same; for coarse adjustment, the pendulum rod is screw-threaded where it enters the collar of the yoke holding the mercury jar.

The system works well, but there are drawbacks. Mercury is a very dense material, and its fumes, in certain conditions, are poisonous; also, the glass jar is a fragile thing, especially in a portable clock, so had to be used only in large regulators and bracket clocks that were not intended to be truly portable. The mercury system reappeared in the nineteenth century in the French and American 'four-glass' clocks, the better-quality French alabaster and slate clocks and, as a 'mock' mercury pendulum, for decoration only, in the German and American mantel clocks of the late nineteenth century.

The Harrison grid-iron pendulum is a different animal altogether. It is a bi-metallic compensating system, working to the principle discovered and propounded by Robert Hooke (see Chapter 2 for Hooke's contribution to earlier horology) that different metals expand by different amounts given the same temperature increase. Thus, as in the mercury system, if one metal expands downwards, and another metal can be made to expand upwards by the same amount, then the effective length of the pendulum will remain constant. In the eighteenth century there were no exotic alloys with low coefficients of expansion, the two most common metals being brass and steel. Brass and steel expand in the ratio of 5:4, and therefore five steel rods expanding one way would expand the same distance as four brass rods, of equivalent length, expanding the other way. Providing the ratio is maintained, the actual number of rods may vary; one could use, say, ten steel rods and eight brass rods, or some lesser quantity than four and five, providing that the *equivalent* lengths are calculated correctly.

In his pendulums, however, Harrison always used four brass rods and five steel ones, connected as shown in figure 19. The obvious advantages of the system were that it could be treated (or maltreated) as a normal pendulum in portable bracket clocks, it was cheaper than the mercury pendulum and it was not too susceptible to accidental damage. It found favour for expensive bracket clocks, and 'mock' versions of it reappeared in (of course) German and American mantel clocks in the late nineteenth century.

As far as bracket-clock styles are concerned in this period, the true bell-top case design had appeared around 1740 (see figure 15), but its popularity nowhere near matched that of the inverted bell top, both styles continuing in general use until the end of the eighteenth century. A more significant development appeared in 1760, a contribution by John Ellicott of the notable clockmaking family of Ellicotts. This was the 'circular' dial and was a radical move away from the traditional style of the bracket clock—so radical that it was to be another ten years before it found favour with the buying public. The outline of one particular clock by John Ellicott is shown in figure 20; in fact, the dial is not circular but a square shape—it is the bezel fitted to the door that is circular, giving

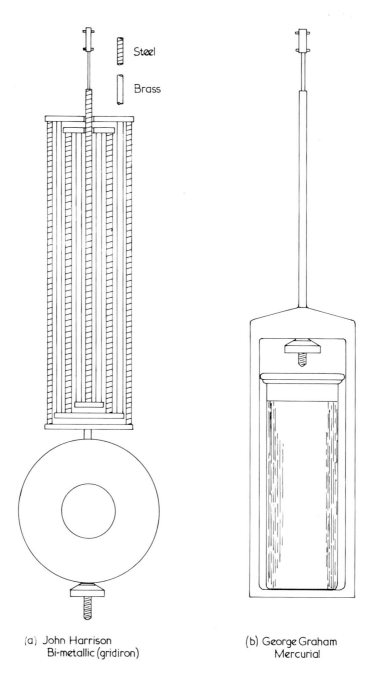

Steel

Brass

(a) John Harrison
    Bi-metallic (gridiron)

(b) George Graham
    Mercurial

Figure 19   Temperature-compensated pendulums

Figure 20 Clock case with apparently circular dial, though it is the bezel in the door which is circular. By John Ellicot, c1750

the impression that the dial is too. Perhaps this design was too radical and inelegant for a customer familiar with the square dial with spandrels and a separate chapter ring; even though Ellicott's clocks were of the finest quality, most buyers still preferred earlier styles. At about the same date, 1760, a new design of minute hand appeared on both bracket and long-case clocks. This was the 'serpentine' form, figure 21; the style may have been copied from French clocks of the period, but this is only surmise—certainly no other change occured, the hour hand remaining non-matching, but by now of lesser artistry.

Figure 21 Serpentine hands, c1750

The dominant furniture style of the period was that of Chippendale, but there were few clocks made to his designs. One reason for this was that the Clockmakers Company, and British clockmakers generally, held the idea that the movement was the dominant feature; the case was a secondary consideration, and the idea of making clocks especially to fit the cases of a furniture designer was anathema to them. The second reason, and a more practical one, was that Chippendale's suggestions for clock cases demonstrated a total lack of knowledge about the workings of clocks. The majority of the cases illustrated in his style book, *The Director*, required specially-made dials for both longcase and bracket clocks; indeed, in one of the longcase styles, there was insufficient width for a 1 second pendulum to swing. Most of them were also too ornate to be used as clocks. The bracket-clock cases included delicate, carved wooden finials and case tops—had these been of brass they might have been acceptable, but in a clock that was more prone than most furniture to damage by transport or by juvenile prying fingers, they would be a disaster. Chippendale's suggestion for a 'full-arch' style of bracket-clock case was quite attractive, however, and was a design which would appear in the early nineteenth century, to be copied in the late nineteenth century (it will be discussed in the next section); but in the middle eighteenth century it was too radical an idea for clockmakers to accept.

THE BREAK-ARCH CASE

One furniture designer who did gain eventual acceptance, if not of his exact designs then of his general ideas, was Hepplewhite. Some of his earlier designs were, as Chippendale's, unsuitable for a clock case, but one style that caught the imagination was the 'break-arch' case, which appeared in about 1770. The case shown in figure 22 echoed the general, if not specific, feeling of his design, but more significantly it necessitated the use of a circular dial. Ellicott had used this idea over ten years

Figure 22   Break-arch case, c1775

previously, but in his design the whole front section of the case formed the door of the clock, revealing a square dial behind the door. The Hepplewhite design was more suited to a circular 'door' covering only the dial area; in other words, we see here the first use of the 'brass bezel', a brass ring into which a piece of moulded glass was plastered, fixed to the case by a single hinge. The prevalent fashion was still the silvered chapter ring on a brass-sheet dial, and the circular dial, necessitated by the break-arch case, was a break in tradition. Spandrels, of course, were no longer needed and manufacture could be simplified: whatever the solution, it was bound to be a more economical way of manufacturing a dial. The dials could be painted, using standard oil-based paints, but in middle-market bracket clocks they were more likely to be stove-enamelled white, using a ceramic firing technique. Here the bracket clock, with its relatively small dial, scored over the longcase; longcase dials were enamelled, but on the large surface area it was difficult to obtain an even curing of the enamel, 'blow-holes' appeared, and there was a tendency to crack with less than perfect handling. The more expensive bracket-clock dials could still be silvered, except that, here, the dial itself would be of brass, a suitably open-pored material on which to bond the thin layer of silver; a painted or enamelled dial could now be made of iron, a cheaper alternative.

In order to match the general form of the case, the dial (and bezel glass) would be of convex form, the heavier cast-brass bezel almost always having a lock on the left-hand side of the case. In theory the lock should be on the left, with the hinge on the right, so that one is opening the door away from the space needed to wind the clock; however, with these circular bezel clocks today, it is wise to support the bezel whilst winding the clock, as the single hinge is likely to have a fairly tenuous hold on the woodwork. One has to support the bezel in the left hand while winding the clock with the right hand—not ergonomically ideal, especially since even left-handed people, because of the clockwise rotation of the key, seem to wind a clock with the right hand. However, eighteenth-century designers could only design for the immediate future, and the right-hand hinge/left-hand lock was, in a new clock, the most convenient layout. Coincidentally, the first 'painted-dial' longcase clock also appeared during this period. Although the earlier forms of bracket-clock cases lingered on, the new fashion gained ground, slowly at first.

The case with a break-arch top needed different treatment than that of previous designs; the break-arch itself needed supports if it was to appear as a completed form. These were usually supplied as Corinthian columns or else as reeded pillars, sometimes fashioned in brass, but more often in wood with brass capitals. The large area beneath the dial was now of course part of the case and could be included in the general ornamentation. Its treatment varied from inlays of light-coloured woods, such as sandalwood, in a geometric design, to an intricate brass fretwork, backed by silk to exclude the dust. The sides of the case would be cut out in an arch form and filled with brass or wood fretwork, the simplest design being the fishscale form; again this fretwork would be backed by silk. It is unusual to find original glass side-panels in a clock of this type—the glass, if found, is usually in replacement for broken or missing fretwork.

The handle, on a case of the pure form, could no longer be at the top of the case, and so here we see a pair of handles, breaking up the plain area of the case sides. The rear door of the clock was usually an arch-shaped glass panel. The case material, for both this style and the inverted bell-top, was by now usually mahogany, although ebony veneer could still be had. A cheaper substitute for ebony, known as 'ebonising', was developed during this period: the case was stained black and then polished.

In about 1780–85, to add to the confusion, a further case style appeared, the type usually known as a 'full-arch', called at that time by a much more graphic name, the 'round-top' (figure 23). It has been suggested that the design was influenced by the work of Sheraton; it is sometimes said to be a natural development of the Hepplewhite break-arch style, and not being an expert in furniture designs I cannot disagree; the full-arch style seems to echo the 'smoothing' influence that Sheraton had on the design of furniture. Apart from the basic difference of the

Figure 23 Full-arch case, 1785

arch, the break-arch and the full-arch case styles exhibit very similar decoration and fittings.

One of the problems encountered with this type of case is the durability of the surface veneer. Especially in the full-arch type, where the veneer runs in one piece over the whole length of the top and both sides, it is easily split by any distortion in the case carcase, as can be seen on many old clocks. Mahogany veneer on a mahogany carcase was an attempt, at least, to overcome the problem of different expansion and contraction rates. If the clock could be kept in a dark, slightly damp atmosphere, then it would probably be in pristine condition, but clocks are functional things and we put them where we can easily see them, so they are subjected to sunlight, dust and, in modern homes, a central-heating system that not only heats up the clock case but takes away the atmospheric moisture.

By the time of the full-arch case, 1780, the majority of bracket-clock movements were using the recoil escapement system, although some makers continued with the crownwheel system.

This period in the development of the bracket clock, with its confusion of styles—inverted bell-top, true bell-top, break-arch case and full-arch case—all in simultaneous production, reflected the general social and international climate of the last quarter of the eighteenth century. This was perhaps, one of the most depressing periods in English history; beginning with the American War of Independence in 1775 and continuing until the French Revolution at the turn of the century (and the problems that *that* would bring in the next century), the glory that was England became tarnished. The inevitable disruption in trade routes benefitted the English clockmaker in the domestic markets and potentially serious competition from the French makers was at least held in abeyance, if for no other reason than patriotic spirit. No one, in those days, could bring into question the ultimate supremacy of the English armed services; the Navy, in particular, had not only the finest seamen but the advantage of John Harrison's chronometer.

England was still a wealthy nation by the standards of those days. But the American War had been draining the exchequer for years and simultaneous campaigns on the Indian continent and against European upstarts were destined to cost a great deal of money. Included in the recoupment plans devised by Prime Minister Pitt was a tax on the clocks and watches in the home—the Act of Parliament, of 1797, was in force for only one year but had a serious effect on the bracket-clock market. Clocks of less than 20s (£1) in value were exempt from the tax, but since bracket clocks of even mediocre quality cost £4–£5 at that time, they and the longcase clocks were hit hardest; gold watches suffered the most severe tax of all. The annual tax was 5s on a clock, 10s on a gold watch and 2s 6d on a silver or other metal watch—not a fortune today, but in 1797 the weekly wage of a labourer would have been only about 5s. Oddities often creep into legislation, and one here was the clause that if your house had less than ten windows, you would be exempt from the tax. So if your house had eleven windows it would be profitable to pay a bricklayer a shilling to brick one up! Clock dealers, sellers and makers were likewise taxed, at the annual rate of 2s 6d if they traded within the City of London or 1s if they traded in the provinces.

Either the collection of such dues became more of a burden than it was worth, or the total income did not justify the aggravation of the middle and upper class; in any case, the Act was repealed in 1798. It was never a major threat to the survival of clockmaking in England. Far more serious, as the eighteenth century drew to a close, was the repercussion of the wars on the demand for clocks. A country at war cannot indulge in the patronage of artists of any kind and its monied citizens were contributing to the war effort in many ways, not all of them voluntary; the market for the more expensive bracket clock was depressed over the next few years. England was not alone in this respect. The French Revolution of 1789 had put paid in that country to royal and wealthy patronage, a state that would exist for over twenty years, and the war with England had virtually killed off mutual trade for the time being. However, clockmaking survived to consolidate once more, and to leave the eighteenth century on a more hopeful note, we will examine a bracket clock that demonstrates several transition features, from a clock of definitive mid-eighteenth-century style to one of definitive early nineteenth-century style. Photograph 8 illustrates a clock by Hedge of Colchester.

The prominent feature is the bracket, which as we saw in Chapter 1 is the exception rather than the rule. This bracket is possibly original, as the mouldings and the curvature of the front apron match those of the clock itself; if it is not original, it is a sympathetic addition. The clock dates from about 1775 and has a 'shallow' version of the Hepplewhite break-arch top case, but here this is matched not by a circular dial (which would not yet have taken hold in the provinces) but by a break-arch dial. The carrying handle retains the earlier position at the apex of the clock, as in the bell-top style, and the full-width door must, of necessity, have an arch top, to follow the contours of the case; the earlier style would have had a more easily manufactured flat top. There are delicate columns supporting the break-arch, since unlike on the circular-dial version, these columns cannot intrude to any degree into the narrow area between the side of the clock and the dial surround. The fretwork at the side of the

8 John Hedge clock, c1775—with bracket

clock, of fish-scale form, is of a design that was to remain popular for over forty years; this is of brass, as are the ogee-shaped feet. The whole of the clock is veneered in mahogany and, although a mixture of styles, it has pleasing proportions.

The dial is of one-piece brass and is silvered all over—not a sign of a spandrel anywhere—resulting in a dial that is easy to read, functional rather than exotic. We also find longcase clocks of this period with all-over silvered dials their own transition from brass to painted dial.

The strike/silent lever is in its usual position in the break-arch and the calendar mechanism is, as usual, below the central arbor, except that here there is no large rotating disc but a small pointer. This type of calendar device is less prone to wear than the former type and is similar to the calendar device found on longcase clocks of the period.

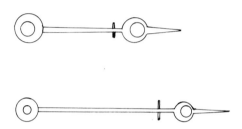

Figure 24 Cross-moonpoise hands, c1775

The style of the hands, figure 24, has no definite classification in clock-making terminology—I would term them 'cross-moonpoise' since the nineteenth-century development of this particular style was either the 'crossed-open spade' or the 'moonpoise' (illustrated on page 90). The main point to note is that the hands are now 'matching': the hour hand is a smaller version of the minute hand. If the hands on this clock are original, going back to 1775, then they anticipate the introduction of matching hands on longcase clocks by some ten years.

Turning to the movement, a most significant change is observed. The all-over engraving has now disappeared, to be replaced by edge-engraving, a feature to continue for many years. On this clock the signature is within a nicely engraved cartouche, a feature to be found, in the future, only on the more expensive clocks.

The movement is a double fusee drive to the going and strike trains, the strike being a single bell, struck on the hour. The recoil escapement is original, with its large lenticular pendulum-bob, and the pendulum latch is in the usual position for a recoil escapement; with its small arc of swing the pendulum rod of a recoil-escapement clock cannot be latched over to one side in the manner of the crown-wheel type.

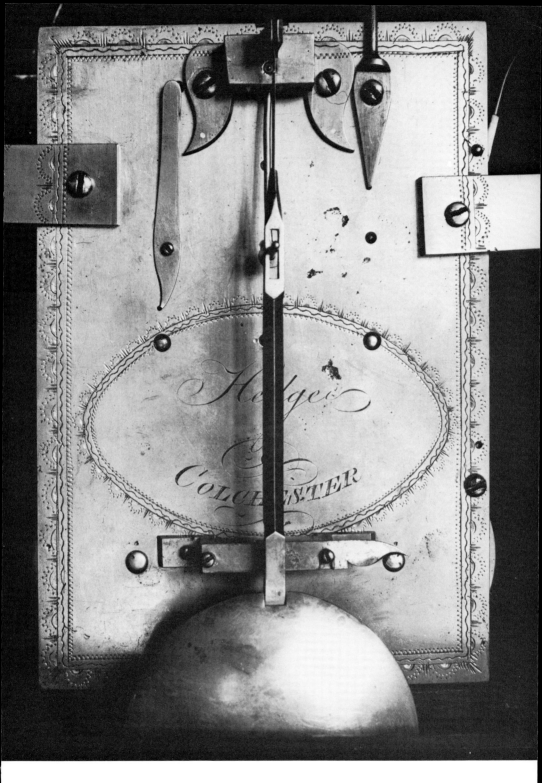

9 Rear of John Hedge clock, showing edge engraving

THE HEDGE FAMILY

The clock was made, as stated previously, by Hedge, but there were four generations of this clockmaking family working in Colchester during the years 1730–1850. At the date of this clock, one John Hedge was in partnership with his brother Thomas, and although it is possible that the clock was made by yet another brother Nathaniel (in independent business at the same period), the all-over silvered dial on both bracket and longcase clocks is a hallmark of the John and Thomas partnership. The detail is confused by the fact that their father Nathaniel was not only a prodigious clockmaker, but a prodigious producer! He lived to be eighty-five, unusual for those days, outlived two wives, and had children as follows:

Sarah	born 1734	died 1735
Nathaniel	born 1735	died 1821
John	born 1737	died 1778
Charles	born 1738	died 1742
Sarah	born 1740	died 1742
William	born 1742	died 1746
James	born 1743	died 1743
Thomas	born 1744	died 1814
Joseph	born 1746	died 1746

The circumstances of the elder Nathaniel's first marriage give a fascinating insight into eighteenth-century social life. He was apprenticed in 1728 to John Smorthwait, a famous Colchester clockmaker, but Nathaniel's talents did not extend only to clockmaking; he and John's daughter Sarah were lovers and in 1733 she became pregnant. This was a catastrophe, not only for Nathaniel, who had served only five years of his seven-year apprenticeship, but also for Sarah, whose father was a prominent citizen and a churchwarden! It was obvious that the poor apprentice would not be accepted as a suitor, so the couple married in secret in a village church outside Colchester. The events must have aged Nathaniel, since the marriage licence gives his age as twenty-six when in fact he was twenty-three—but he would have falsified the record so that his age matched Sarah's: it was considered unseemly for a man to marry an older woman. On revealing the marriage to John Smorthwait, the couple were turned out onto the street, and John never again acknowledged the existence of his daughter, even leaving her out of his will. Nathaniel was taken into partnership by William Cooper, and when John Smorthwait died in 1739 was able to buy the business from John's widow. The Hedge family was dogged with ill-luck and many of their children died in infancy; but one, Nathaniel junior, survived to a ripe old age. Nathaniel and his brother John formed a successful partnership which lasted until John died in 1778 (though the clock described here was made by John while in partnership with Thomas). In 1807, at the age of seventy-two Nathaniel junior went into partnership with Joseph Banister, who carried on the clockmaking business when Nathaniel retired from active work in 1814. A clock by this partnership will be described in the next chapter.

6

TOWARDS AND AWAY FROM
ELEGANCE, 1800–1850

By the turn of the century, the population of the United Kingdom was around 10.5 million; since 1700 there must have been an extra 50,000 people with the money to buy a good class of bracket clock. But the mix of this market was changing. Britain was over one hundred years into the industrial-nation epoch and new fortunes were being made, not only in war supplies, but in general manufacturing—wool and cotton, coal, iron and other branches of engineering. We now had the age of the industrialists, the independent farmers, the shipowners, engineers and others to vie with the merchants and landowners for middle-class status.

In its buying habits, this 'nouveau riche' did not set trends but followed the pundits; to be *seen* to be successful, one must have the latest designs of the 'in' people. Chippendale, by now, was 'out', and although the more graceful designs of Robert Adam lingered on into the nineteenth century, three names were prominent on the middle and upper-class shopping list—Hepplewhite, Sheraton and Hope. Hepplewhite had died in 1786, but the popularity of his style was such that his *Cabinet Makers' and Upholsterers' Guide* was still in print by the end of the century. His designs had the lightness of the Adam style, with elegant curves and tapering legs to tables and chairs; many incorporated fine inlay work and he is credited with the first use of the Prince-of-Wales-feathers motif.

Sheraton, who died in 1806, used the same light style, his furniture being instantly recognisable as the type one dreads to lean on, since the legs never appear to be strong enough to carry the upperworks, let alone anything else! This was an illusion, of course, since many items of his furniture have survived to the present day, and he was a master of his craft. He published several books on furniture design which were an immediate success, largely because his style was a development from Adam and Hepplewhite and not something radically different.

One bracket-clock case style that matched this classical outlook was the 'balloon' case, a logical development of the French 'waisted' style and one that could be made in wood, rather than the elaborate materials used by the earlier French makers. This style, illustrated in figure 25,

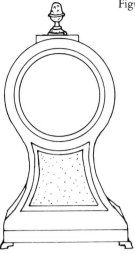

Figure 25 Balloon case, c1790, a development of the French 'waisted' style

was, in the main, the product of English makers, and the majority of examples have standard English double-fusee movements, in cases of mahogany, inlaid on the front apron. One of the problems that faced English manufacturers here was that the clock case had to be large enough to fit the double-fusee movement—not such a problem in the eighteenth century, but in the nineteenth century cases in general became smaller. Following Waterloo and the establishing of the second French Empire came a revival of the import of French clocks, and they had comparatively small-sized movements is could easily be brought down in size as the century progressed. The English makers chose not to follow their lead, retaining the fusee drive on each train; in truth, the use of a fusee on the strike side was an unnecessary expense in a competitive market. As clocks became smaller in order to blend with furniture styles, English makers could not compete, except to make the clock as a timepiece only; in the first quarter of the nineteenth century it cost as much to buy an English timepiece movement as to buy a French one with hour and half-hour strike, on a bell. By about 1810, therefore, the English makers had turned to more recent styles, leaving the French to continue unchallenged in this particular style.

Thomas Hope was something else—a wealthy · amateur, whose extensive travels throughout Greece, Italy and Egypt, prompted him to publish, in 1807, his *Household Furniture and Design*. The designs, mainly for furniture, show a mixture of French Empire and English Romanticism; by the time the book was published, Nelson had won the Battle of the Nile and perhaps this was what gripped the imagination of the public, more than the quality of the designs. A sample of Hope's clock designs is the ormolu and bronze mantel clock in the King's Apartments at the Royal Pavilion, Brighton. Concomitant with the

Empire Design is the use of the lion motif—this was exhibited in the earlier French designs and reappears in the English Empire style. Probably the most magnificent piece of furniture with this motif is the sideboard-cupboard, at Brighton, displaying both head and feet of the lion on the vertical supports. The lion appears on clocks in the early part of the nineteenth century, for its popularity was consolidated after the Battle of Waterloo. The monument to the battle is a reclining lion, cast in bronze from captured French guns sitting atop a man-made hill, facing towards France. The popular story was that the lion was put there to remind France of the folly of making war with England and faced that direction as a warning against future encroachment. Waterloo was the biggest boost to national morale that England had experienced for many a year, and national fervour was reflected in both furniture and clock design.

GOTHIC REVIVAL STYLES

On the architectural front two campaigns in process at the start of the nineteenth century immediately affected the design of the bracket clock. Throughout the later eighteenth century, there had been a growing interest in the revival of the Gothic style (or as it is sometimes termed, with quaint patriotism, Saxon style), the dominant features being the Norman arch and the trefoil window. This revival was still in full swing at the turn of the century, competing with the classical style of building that we associate with the Regency period. The eighteenth-century Gothic protagonist had been Samuel Wyatt, but at the dawn of the next century it was William Hopper who became a household name in Gothic architecture. If it was the classical style you wanted for your new house (or castle), it was to John Nash you would go, and there was heated competition between the two architects. Nash was responsible for the design of Shane's Castle in Ireland, but before he had completed the work he was replaced by Hopper, perhaps explaining the Gothic feeling of the final edifice. Nash landed *the* contract of the early nineteenth century—the remodelling of the Brighton Pavilion, a style which did not suit Hopper although he had already built a Gothic conservatory for the Prince Regent at Carlton House.

The influence of architecture and furniture design was fostered and furthered by Royal patronage. The Royal Pavilion, started in the 1780s and finished in 1822, with the work of making its various furnishings, employed the English Empire-stylists for many years. Hopper's Gothic masterpiece was Penrhyn Castle in Wales, not completed until 1837 when the Gothic revival had almost run its course.

This period in particular brought a radical change to the case design of

Figure 26 The Gothic case, which appeared in 1800

bracket clocks. Throughout the eighteenth century, the clockmakers had dictated a case design to match their movements, but as the nineteenth century dawned so did the realisation that clocks would have to come to terms with furniture design; from 1800 onwards we see clock cases faithfully following fashions of the time, with only the occasional revival of an earlier style. The first new case style of the nineteenth century was the Gothic one (sometimes called the 'lancet' top, though I shall refer to it by its architectural synonym), illustrated in figure 26. It appeared in about 1800 and continued to be made until the end of the particular Gothic revival in about 1835–40. The case of these clocks was usually finished in ebony veneer, or was ebonised, a finish suiting the sombre mood of its surroundings at that time, though some cases were given a mahogany veneer. There are examples where the ebonising has been stripped off to expose the mahogany carcase, after a change in fashion dictated a lighter style of case. Decoration was fairly minimal, usually limited to brass 'string' inlay on the front apron and in the arch. A more detailed examination of this style may be made by a study of the clock shown in photographs 10 and 11; this clock is signed by Hedge and Banister, Colchester, and dates from about 1810. The case is of ebony finish, with brass inlay to the apron and the arch. The arch is of true Gothic form (take this clock to Penrhyn Castle, and it would match the doorway arches found there). The only external adornments are the solid brass 'caddy-ball' feet and the brass handles to the case sides; the handles are of the lion's-head motif and exhibit definite signs of English Empire styling, but here the mixture of Empire and Gothic is successful: the

10 Hedge & Banister clock, c1810, a mixture of Empire and Gothic

menacing lion's head matches the brooding impression of the clock. The fretwork to the sides is not, in this example, in the usual fish-scale design, but follows a pattern that would be found in, say, a leaded lattice within a Gothic-arch window—a complementary conclusion to the case style.

The dial is convex within a brass bezel which, unusually (and more ergonomically), is hinged on the left. The lettering of the dial is clear and uncomplicated and the dial plate is fitted with shrouds to the winding holes, protecting the painted surface from criminal assault with the winding key. The hands are of the crossed moonpoise type, almost an identical pair to those on the clock by Hedge, photograph 8, and a style which suited this type of clock.

11 Rear of Hedge & Banister clock, showing shaped back plate

The movement exhibits a further development of bracket clocks in general. The square (or rectangular) back plate had now given way to a shaped design, as shown here, with shoulders to the top and a cutaway section at the bottom, one advantage of the cutaway being a surer seating of the movement on the seatboard. The back plate is edge-engraved, as would be the norm by this date, and the signature, behind the bell, is merely that—without the elaboration of a cartouche. In the years to follow, edge-engraving disappeared but the basic shape of the back plate remained in this style. The single bell, striking the hours only, is mounted on the back plate, as are virtually all of those in Gothic cases, since a Gothic arch has insufficient space for a bell to sit atop the movement. The movement itself is typically English—a double fusee drive, with recoil escapement and heavy lenticular pendulum-bob; any supporting brackets, or cocks, have nicely finished tails.

Hedge and Bannister were producing their own clocks when many other provincial makers had taken the option to buy their movements from the London workshops; the movement in this clock, although it has the look of a production unit, may therefore have been made in their own workshops. The Hedge of this partnership was Nathaniel, the elder brother of the previously mentioned John Hedge, whose clock is shown in photograph 8. Joseph Banister was a highly skilled clockmaker whose claim to horological fame was a superb longcase regulator, with an improved Graham dead-beat escapement and a massive mercury

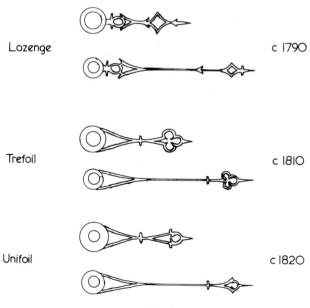

Lozenge   c 1790

Trefoil   c 1810

Unifoil   c 1820

Figure 27 Hand styles 1790–1820

pendulum. He also made wall regulators for other retailers to use as their master clocks; a copy of his longcase regulator was made for the Duke of Sussex, but the Duke died before it was ready—unfortunately for the Duke but fortunately for our heritage, since the clock was eventually bought for the Mason collection of Colchester Clocks, now in the care of Colchester Borough Coucil. The partnership lasted from 1807 until 1814, when Hedge retired.

The Gothic ethos also gave rise to the development of various hand styles, the most popular being the Gothic 'trefoil', similar to the window design of Gothic churches and castles. This first appeared in about 1810, and is illustrated in figure 27, together with a further development, which for want of a standard name I shall call the 'unifoil'. These hands were in use throughout the Gothic period, although many variations on the theme were offered during the period 1810–40.

SHERATON–EMPIRE STYLES

The Sheraton–Empire vogue also influenced the design of clock cases. In about 1810 the 'chamfer'-top case appeared. If any clock symbolised the return to elegance of the true Regency period, this was surely it. The case, illustrated in figure 28, was easy to manufacture, since there were

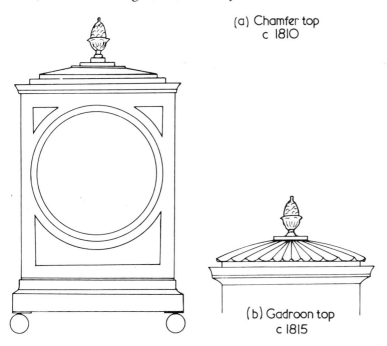

(a) Chamfer top
c 1810

(b) Gadroon top
c 1815

Figure 28   The chamfer-top case and later development, the gadroon top

no long runs of curved veneering, and exhibits a symmetry of proportion that the Gothic arch never quite achieved. The majority of these clocks were veneered in 'good-grained' woods, such as mahogany or rosewood, which matched the style of the furniture they were intended to complement. Most examples show the return of the spandrel, leading one's eye naturally to the dial. In fact the spandrels are a part of the case design, rather than the dial design, and are usually inset panels, framed in brass quadrant. The chamfered top often supported a brass finial, more correctly called a terminal, with a pineapple motif; occasionally the terminal would be in the French 'flambeau' or flaming-torch style—at first glance the two types are very similar. Although the Empire style demanded lion's-head handles and perhaps lion's-paw feet, the chamfer top would almost always have the 'rosette' style of handles, with caddy-ball feet, a less menacing combination that suited the overall elegance of the case. A slightly later development of the top was the 'gadroon' style, sometimes simply called 'fluted' or 'reeded', illustrated in figure 28b.

As the Gothic case style gave rise to its particular style of hands, so the Sheraton Empire case style demanded a co-ordinated pair of hands, and several designs around a basic style appeared during the first fifteen years of the nineteenth century. The two parent styles were the 'spade' and the 'moonpoise'—illustrated in figure 29—the spade so called for its resemblance to the trenching spade in use at this time (and used also on playing cards). In the moonpoise, the drilled hole is not concentric within the basic circle at the tip of this hand, giving the effect of a crescent-moon

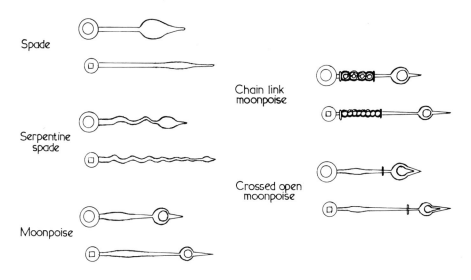

Figure 29   Hand styles 1800–1825

shape to the remaining metal; the hand however, does not terminate at the moon: there is a further tapering section beyond it, correctly called a 'poise' (a similar extension on the other side of the hand arbor would be termed a 'counter-poise'). So, the full definition of the style is moon-and-poise, but this is usually shortened to moonpoise. The design of this hand is attributed to Abraham-Louis Breguet, the French master of chronometer and watch manufacture, who used the style to decorate the majority of his watches.

Elaborations of these two styles included the serpentine spade and the 'chain-link' moonpoise, shown in figure 29; by the time these hands arrived, they must mostly have been mass-produced, since even the more elaborate designs turn up in clocks manufactured in widespread geographical locations and only on rare occasions do we find a set of hands made to special order.

A clock representative of this period, illustrated in photographs 12 and 13, is signed Archard, London; it is reputed to date from 1817 (but more of this later). The clock stands 16 inches high and is 11½ inches wide, 7½ inches deep. The case is in the full-arch style of the Sheraton school and is veneered in 'flame' mahogany, with a geometric line inlay of either satinwood or boxwood. The full-arch case had been available since the 1780s and was a style in its own right; Cescinsky and Webster, in their book *English Domestic Clocks* (an excellent pictorial record of case styles), suggest that the full-arch style with the additon of terracing and terminals to the top of the case was a Hope Empire style, and that the full arch only was a simpler version of this style. I would submit that the Hope Empire upperworks were an addition to an already existing style—the full arch.

The fittings on this clock consist of lion's-head motif carrying-handles and beautifully cast lion's-paw feet, very similar in style to those used in the sideboard-cupboard in the Brighton Pavilion mentioned previously. The feet are undoubtedly the original ones, but the handles are recent replacements—probably, however, the original handles too were of a lion's-head design, to match the feet.

The fretwork at the sides of the case is the usual (by this time) fish-scale design, executed in brass, which was then chemically blackened. The brass bezel with convex glass covers a convex iron dial, 8 inches in diameter, with painted ground and numerals; the strike/silent lever is housed in a slot above the numeral XII, the usual position in a full-arch case. The hands are of the crossed open-moonpoise design, a development of the Breguet moonpoise, and since they incorporate a shaped root section, our watch-making colleagues would, more correctly, define them as a development of the Breguet 'Empire' style, as distinct from the

12 Clock labelled 'Archard', c1817

13 Rear view of 'Archard' clock
with unexpected rectangular plates

Breguet 'straight' style, which has a straight root section. This style of hands was to prove popular during the period 1810–30; although they were mass-produced, the delicacy of the cutaway sections imparted an impression of at least a little craftsmanship.

The movement is the typical English style of fusees for both going and strike trains, the strike being the hours only, on a single bell. There is a pull-repeat system, with star-wheel and click, as yet a functional device, since we are still at least ten years away from the introduction of gas lighting and, therefore, any convenient means of reading the time at night. The striking is, of course, by the rack and snail method and the escapement is of the recoil (anchor) type with heavy lenticular pendulum-bob.

There are two distinctive features of this movement. The first is that the plates are rectangular, when by the stated date of 1817 we would expect shouldered plates, with the bottom section cut away, similar to the movement shown in photograph 11; however, this could be passed off as an anachronistic lapse (with slight uncertainty). The edge, or border, engraving is certainly in keeping with a date between 1800 and 1820, after which time it is found only on isolated examples.

The second feature is not apparent from a cursory inspection of the movement, except for the fact that on the front plate is the serial number 6179, hand-punched into the brass. However, under one of the supporting brackets is stamped the legend 'I. Thwaites'. A look at the clockmaking industry may suggest the origins of this particular clock.

THWAITES AND REED

The 'I. Thwaites' of the legend refers to John Thwaites (the letter I was a common substitute for J). The original clockmaker of this name, as a company, first appears in 1740, as Aynsworth Thwaites; later the company was known as Aynsworth and John Thwaites, then (presumably on the death or retirement of Aynsworth) simply as John Thwaites, before finally becoming Thwaites and Reed in about 1810. The company traded under this name until quite recently; the name is retained, but it has been taken over by Elliotts. This company retained their complete trading records, virtually intact from the eighteenth century until the time they ceased trading as a separate company in the 1970s; these are now lodged with the Guildhall, London, and provide a fascinating insight into the life of a clockmaker, especially in Regency times.

The Thwaites and Reed records destroy the myth that a clock signed 'Fred Bloggs, London' could only have been made by Fred Bloggs; they list many people, some within the higher echelons of clockmaking, to whom they supplied either complete clocks or movements only. The clock illustrated in photograph 9, by Nathaniel Hedge, Colchester, is a case in point. The Thwaites records show that in 1794 they supplied Hedge with a wall-dial clock, and over the next ten years or so he purchased a total of eight other clocks. Without suggesting that the particular clock illustrated was not made by Hedge—I have not had the opportunity to examine it in detail—this certainly confirms that the name on the dial does not necessarily indicate the provenance of the clock movement. As an example, in March 1801 Thwaites and Reed supplied to Hedge of Colchester 'a spring clock with 7 inch silvered dial plate, flat pendulum, in a mahogany roundtop case'. 'Flat pendulum' was then the usual term for the lenticular-bob pendulum, to distinguish it from the round-bob pendulum of the crown-wheel escapement, still at that time in limited production; 'roundtop' was a simple descriptive term for the full-arch case style. So Hedge was supplied with a bracket clock with a 7 inch diameter silvered dial (good quality, this one), in a mahogany full-arch case, the movement having recoil escapement with lenticular-bob pendulum.

A short list of some nineteenth-century clockmakers who were house-hold names, is shown below, together with the total numbers of clocks or movements supplied to each by Thwaites and Reed.

Barraud, Paul	74
Barwise, John	11
Congreve, William	see below
Ellicott, John	183
Ellicott and Co	38
Hedge, Nathaniel	9
Perigal and Dutterrau	21
Tupman	3
Vulliamy, Benjamin and Justin	3
Yonge, George	27

This is only a minute proportion of the total output of this Clerkenwell workshop and is useful in showing the extent to which these bought-in clocks were used by other clock makers. I have included Sir William Congreve in the list, not because he was a known maker of standard clocks, but because, during the early years of the century, he was perfecting his 'rolling-ball clock', a device which even today is copied copiously, not as a superb timekeeper but as an object of almost hypnotic fascination. The Thwaites records list various jobs done for him during the years 1801–08, and it is obvious that they were concerned with the rolling-ball clock; the invoice descriptions seem uncertain on the names for the particular items—they are variously listed as 'quantities of brass turnings', 'brass millings' and the like! Congreve patented his device in 1808 and, whilst in military circles (he was an artillery officer) he will probably be remembered for his invention of a rocket missile, he has gone into horological history as the inventor of the rolling-ball clock; he owes some thanks to Thwaites and Reed!

As a further example of the diversity of clock manufacturing and selling during the early nineteenth century, I have reproduced a shipping order from the Thwaites records for July 1802. Unfortunately, in the age of the quill pen and the flowing style of handwriting, some of the words defy translation, and my interpretation of the written word is given in parenthesis.

July 1802   For Mr Hynam
    Shipp'd on board [the?] John Matt Nicholson

i   To a Spring quarter clock with 8½″ japanned dial plate in quarters upon 8 bells, flat pendulum and metal hands gilt in a mahogany case with brass columns fluted.

   [Trusses] at side raised [——]. 2 large frets in front pannells, Brass ring and Convex   y(?) – AC – 0
                                                                                                               [£27 – 16 – 0]

ii To a spring quarter clock as above in mahogany [Truss] case, ¼ columns and large fret in front pannell and [raised] brass ring and convex glass   AH – AW – O
                                                                                                               [£19 – 15 – 0]

iii To 2 best spring clocks with 8½″ japanned [dials?] and plates. Flat pendulums and metal hands gilt in mahogany cases round top, three pannells and pierced frets, [brass-] rings and convex glass   yN – A(?)
                                                                                                               [£23 – 17 – 0]

   To 2 spring clocks with 8″ plates, friezed middles, flat pendulums in mahogany round top cases, one pannell   AH – a(?)
                                                                                                               [£19 – 17 – 0]

iv To a 12″ Round Plate, Japanned and gilt hands   A – AA – O
                                                                                                               [£1 – 11 – 0]

v   To a 12″ Round Plate, friezed middle   A – AO – O
                                                                                                               [£1 – 16 – 0]

To 3 pr. of weight shells and 1 Doz. French gut.	A – (?) – (?) [£1 – 7 – 7]
To 18 Hand Files and to 12 smaller ditto and 3 smooth ditto and 9 rough [rottence?] and 6 smooth ditto	A – H – O [£1 – 9 – 0]
To 3 Packing Cases for which above, plained and with proper packing	y – T – O [2 – 8 – 0]
To Shipping, Duty, Posterage, Lighterage etc.	A – AW – ? [£1 – 15 – 0]
To insurance on policy and bills of lading	A – AA – O [£1 – 11 – 0]

The first problem arising from this account is the curious coding system used for pricing. I have been unable to obtain an 'official' explanation of the code since there does not appear to be a 'code list' in the records, but applying the most commonly used letters in the code (plus an intelligent guess at the odd letters that appear) it is possible to substitute the letters of the name 'AYNSWORTH' for the numbers 1–9. Judging by other prices that were charged at this time, it is a reasonable estimation, but no more; the records from 1840 onwards show real money values and therefore comparisons become easier.

The first six clocks on the list are all bracket clocks of various quality. Item i appears to be a break-arch case (see figure 22), standing about 18in high (to match an 8½in diameter dial and allowing sufficient space for a three-train movement), with carrying handles to the side and fitted with recoil escapement. The only other case that could match this description is a break-arch style, where the top is not round but is in Gothic style—perhaps explaining the use of the term 'trusses', as used in roof trusses. The next four clocks seem to be middle-price items, all in full-arch cases, the first two with brass fretwork both to the sides and to the front panel, the second two of slightly lesser quality; the 'friezed middles', if it refers to the dials, is a mystery—it could refer to the frosting or matting of the dial centre, but that would assume a brass dial, unusual for this period, or it could refer to some external decoration. Items (iv) and (v) are wall dials. The list demonstrates that Thwaites not only supplied clocks but also spare parts and tools. It is unlikely, of course, that they made the hand files mentioned in the order; they would have bought them in from toolmakers to make up a package deal.

(Prescot in Lancashire was one of the areas specialising in the manufacture of hand tools.)

Since the records of Thwaites and Reed are so exhaustive, it is possible to make some assumptions concerning this Archard clock (photographs 12 and 13).

The numbering system for Thwaites' clocks became formalised only in 1842, but it is possible to estimate the date of manufacture of earlier numbers from the occasional reference to a number on invoices and job records. For instance, the number 6179, on the Archard clock, was issued in about 1817–18, but as mentioned earlier the back plate style suggests an earlier date, probably before 1800. Also, by 1817, the firm was known as Thwaites and Reed, and not John Thwaites, that being the name stamped into the brackets, again suggesting a date before the amalgamation of 1810. There is no doubt that the movement and the case were originally intended for each other, since there are no signs within the case of a different movement ever being there, and the engraving runs across the brackets correctly for the angle at which the brackets should be fitted. The case style was popular from 1780–1820, but the hands (seemingly original) limited the period, since they did not appear on clocks before about 1800.

One explanation could be that the movement was old stock (from, say, about 1805) and was not numbered until it was fitted into a conveniently sized case (to fit the brackets) in 1817. The other explanation is that whoever stamped the number picked up the wrong punch, intending to stamp the number 4179, for the year 1808. Not an impossible explanation—there are many known examples of original sins during the manufacture of clocks.

The name on the dial, Archard, does not supply the answer. There is no Thwaites record of a clock supplied to a Mr Archard, nor does anyone of that name appear, at the right time, in reference books or street directories. The London street directories for 1810–20 list a Sam Archer of Hatton Garden, and a Thomas Archer of Smithfield; it is not until the year 1842 that one Thomas Archard appears, and he is listed as a coachmaker, not a clockmaker or retailer. Perhaps, then, the name on the dial is wrong. It is likely that the dial has been repainted at least once during its lifetime—its condition is too fresh to be original to a case that is well 'lived-in'. However, a dial artist is unlikely to have mistaken a faded 'Archer' for 'Archard', even if he might have done the reverse. A possible explanation, for those who like to clear up such uncertainties, could be on these lines. In 1842, Mr Thomas Archard, successful coachmaker of this parish, bought a bracket clock. He could have bought it secondhand from Thwaites and Reed (since they did sell such clocks—and we can ignore the true date of manufacture) or he could have bought it from a retailer. In any case (sic!) the clock was by then at least twenty-five years old and the dial was a little worse for wear; since Mr A. was proud of his new possession, he decided to have his own name painted on the dial, so that he could stand the clock in the window of his office; hence the anomalies.

Further to this problem of dating, I have recently examined in detail a clock very similar to the Archard. Belonging to a local surgeon, this clock was undergoing restoration and is of particular interest because, apart from the front apron (a brass fretwork panel, instead of an inlay) the case style is identical to that of the Archard. The dial is signed George Yonge, London, and knowing that Yonge was a regular customer of the Thwaites workshop (twenty-seven purchases), it was a simple matter to check for a number in an expected place on the movement. Sure enough on the front plate, below the motion work, was the legend:

$$T + R$$
$$5574$$

According to the Thwaites records, this dates the clock from about 1815, despite the presence of an ancient tablet inside the clock case, giving a date of 1798. The curious point is that by 1815 the T + R symbol was being used, but on the Archard clock, supposedly from 1817, the earlier name of John Thwaites appears! I would even hesitate to doubt the scribbled date of 1798—it is not an impossible date for the clock, given that the interpretation of the Thwaites numbering system is in error. Whatever the real story, the foregoing discussion demonstrates that, in the history of clocks, we should take nothing for granted, and concentrated research into a specific area may yield surprising results.

CLOCK CASES AS FURNITURE

The chapter heading refers to a new age of elegance, which I believe was seen in the period 1810–20. Britain was at the height of her European power; although she had waged war, in Europe, America and the East, continuously over the last twenty years (and at a cost of some £700 million), she had doubled her export trade and her revenue. It was to be a shortlived boom, but people made the most of it; 'I doubt whether any community ever attained such a pitch of prosperity and glory,' wrote Lord Dudley, and a writer in 1816 commented that 'The houses of mechanics were crowded with furniture, till they themselves could scarcely turn round in them—clocks, chests of drawers and tables, crowded into the smallest rooms. . . .' The clocks would hardly have been bracket clocks, in the house of a 'mechanic', but could have been Black Forest products, especially wall clocks, which were beginning to appear in big numbers at this time. The increased market for Empire-style furniture would now, of course, be followed by the clockmakers. No longer was the clock case a secondary item, intended merely to house the craftsmanship of the movement: it now followed the dictates of fashion, and was probably made by production-line methods: many of the cases from this period are not only similar but virtually identical—in both construction and finish. Perhaps this was one reason for the decline of the longcase clock: because of its design it was not as adaptable to change as the bracket clock, and could not match the ever-increasing competition during the nineteenth century; certainly it had almost disappeared, on a national scale, by 1850. The bracket clock itself, as a bastion of English clockmaking skill, was to come under siege in its mutation into a mass-market item—its style would weather the onslaught, but its national identity would be lost.

The close of the war with France, and the establishment of the Second Empire, had of course reopened the trade routes with that country and the Empire-style residences now being built were more suited, as a market, to the more ornate and smaller products of the French clockmakers. We have already seen that, in the eighteenth century the large, exotic bracket clocks attained a moderate popularity, but once they were scaled down to suit the proportions of nineteenth-century homes, their free-flowing style was an immediate asset. We now see the waisted bracket clock reducing in size to that of an English bracket clock, but more importantly we see the introduction on an increasing scale of the Second Empire style of clock, with cast figurines, swags of fruit and flowers, 'classical' themes which caught the imagination of the English public. They were not bracket clocks—indeed, they did not look anything like a bracket clock; but their size and design enabled them to be sited in the areas traditionally reserved for the bracket clock—the hall table, the dining-room sideboard, the mantelpiece. Also, many of the buildings erected in the first twenty years of the nineteenth century (Gothic style apart), with their gilt mirrors, glass chandeliers, marble columns and brass-inlaid furniture, held no place for the English bracket clock, with the exception of the chamfer top. This book is concerned only with the bracket clock, until its general transition into the mantel clock in the later years of the nineteenth century, and therefore I cannot embark in detail on the fascinating subject of the French mantel clocks, except to see them in general terms as competitors of the bracket clock. French, German and Austrian clocks were also being imported,

14 Clock by John Cooper, c1825

competing in both the traditional bracket-clock market and the emerging
lower-to-middle class markets.

The next type of clock for more detailed study as representative of this
period is the chamfer top. Appearing in about 1810, and continuing in
popularity until at least 1840, it shows the continuing analogy with
furniture design; the general design has already been discussed and is
illustrated in figure 28a. A particular clock, by Cooper of Colchester, is
shown in photographs 14 and 15; it was made in about 1825 and stands

15 Rear view of John Cooper clock, devoid of engraving

19in high (to the top of the terminal), 11in wide and 7½in deep. The case is in mahogany on a mahogany carcase, with the quarter panels edged in brass quadrant. The pineapple terminal, rosette handles and caddy-ball feet are all of brass, as are the fretwork panels to the case sides; the frets are in the usual fish-scale pattern. The case edges are finished in a 'milled' design, a typical feature of the Sheraton/English Empire style.

The dial is convex, behind a brass bezel, and is painted; the matching hands are of the basic moonpoise design, with the additon of a chain-link design at the root, a slightly more expensive feature than the serpentine form.

The movement is devoid of any engraving, apart from the signature (half hidden by the bell), which from this period on was the norm, except on very expensive clocks. It is a standard, double-fusee, two-train drive, with the strike on the hour only, and the escapement is the recoil type with heavy, lenticular-bob pendulum. This pendulum is adjusted by means of a threaded rod attached to the centre of the bob, instead of the pendulum rod itself being threaded, a type of adjustment that would alternate with the earlier form throughout the nineteenth century. In this particular clock, the pendulum catch, used when carrying the clock, is missing.

The movement plates are the typical shape for this period, with shouldered tops and cutaway bottom sections—indeed, the whole movement of this clock had the look of a jobbing workshop, although I have not been able as yet to verify this. Bernard Mason, in his book *Clock and Watchmaking in Colchester*, lists John Cooper as a 'Trader and Occasional Maker' and I guess that this was *not* one of his occasional makes. Nevertheless, the clock as a whole is a pleasing example of this period.

The 'milled-edge' feature of this clock is, as on many others of its period, imitation: originally a milled finish was achieved by carving from the solid, whereas by 1815 it is usually made up of a series of glued strips, turned or milled from lateral strips. (If the original milled edge was created by carving, what is the term for an edge made by milling?) Cescinsky and Webster, in *English Domestic Clocks*, point to this imitation milling as part of the decadence of English cabinetmaking, but I would suggest that it was an adaptation to suit the changing market, a public becoming ever more fashion and cost conscious; after all, this public was buying a French clock with a craftsmanship content nowhere near that of the English bracket clock, but giving them high fashion at a low price. Nothing has changed—since the evolution of our industrial-based society, there has always been a mass market, and a top 20 per cent who choose and can afford to pay for English craftsmanship.

TOWARDS VICTORIAN SOBRIETY

The emphasis was changing, from 1820 onwards. Added to the traditional London trade were the new rich, with new occupations—mill owner, manufacturer, steelmaker, coal-mine owner, in diverse locations like Manchester, Birmingham and Sheffield. Not only would this new breed of man be wealthy, he would want an overt display of wealth in the latest fashion, for residence and furniture. The white-dial longcase clock enjoyed, for a brief few years, a share in this prosperity; whilst, in London, this type of clock was rapidly running out of favour, the north-country clocks were becoming ever more elaborate. The exotic woods now coming through the Atlantic ports of Bristol and Liverpool allowed lavish decoration to the longcase and whilst the bracket clock tried to beat competition by cheaper manufacturing methods, the longcase competed by becoming not only more expensive but more imposing, until its proportions were lost.

The problem with bracket-clock styles during the 1810–20 period was that Britain had been living in a fool's paradise—and by 1820 the flirtation with an age of elegance was over. The true costs of the European wars were having an effect, and the country entered a depression soon after 1820. Unfortunately for the bracket clock, its newly emerged styles, the chamfer top, Gothic top and gadroon top, like

Figure 30 Full-arch dial with Gothic top

the furniture of the time did not reflect the general feeling of depression. The gadroon top (see figure 28b) had come into more common use in 1810–20. As mentioned earlier, the style is often known as 'reeded' or 'fluted', but gadroon is architecturally more correct, referring to a series of convex curves terminating at a single point. The short-lived full-arch dial (figure 30) also dates from this period. It suited only the Gothic top (as illustrated) and the gadroon top, if the overall proportions were to be maintained, and it disappeared when these did. However, it rose again, phoenix-like, at the end of the century.

As William IV was being enthroned in 1830, faced with the task of revitalising a jaded nation, Thomas Telford, designer and builder of the Menai suspension bridge, was reaching the peak of his career, followed by the young Isambard Kingdom Brunel and George Stephenson the younger. This was the age of the engineers, and their influence was felt throughout British life, bringing a sturdy simplicity of design to furniture and clocks, moving rapidly away from Regency elegance and the by now overburdened Gothic. These were men of plain language and plain tastes—their wives (or mistresses) might choose a French gilt clock for the boudoir, but the dominant household clock would remain an English bracket clock or, in the northern half of the nation, a white-dial longcase clock.

I will be discussing a clock by Vulliamy which is representative of this period, but first, I want to illustrate a clock from the 1830–40 period, a kind of transition from Regency elegance to Victorian sobriety. The clock shown in photograph 16 is by Wright of London, and was made around 1835–40; it stands 18in high to the terminal, and is 10½in wide by 7in deep. The case is veneered in mahogany on a mahogany carcase and is notable for its complete absence of brass decoration; the style is the gadroon top, with a turned mahogany terminal. The top is matched by gadroon-style feet, carved in wood. The corner decoration remains, but here it is of carved wood, separately applied, a feature that was cheaper than brass but still allowed a measure of ornamentation—a feature that would become more popular as the century progressed. There are no carrying handles to this clock, for a reason explained later, and since it is a timepiece only, there are no side frets—indeed even many striking clocks of this period have no side frets. The convex dial is of 8in diameter and of painted iron, by now almost universal for bracket-clock dials; the hands are the 'double-swell' spade type, a development of the simple spade. (These might be a replacement, since the minute hand does not reach the outer edge of the chapter ring; but then the tip could have been broken off by careless handling.) The name on the dial would be that of a retailer, as both case and movement are probably batch-produced items.

16 Clock by Wright of London, c1835

The movement (not illustrated) is the standard English fusee drive, with recoil escapement and heavy lenticular-bob pendulum. The pendulum has a latch for transport purposes, although this clock would not be carried around as much as its seventeenth-century cousin was. The plates are shouldered, with the bottom cut away; the movement itself is completely devoid of decoration and appears to be the product of a jobbing workshop.

The overall plain appearance is indicative of the change that was taking place in all areas of design. The fact that a clock is issued solely as a time-piece does not automatically mean that its case will be cheaper, since there are many such timepieces in elegant cases; it is likely that this case was supplied for the later fitting of either a striking or a timepiece move-ment. One significant feature of this and later clocks is that they adapted along with the changes in domestic life. For instance by 1840 gas lighting was fairly well established, and with this marvel of the age the need for a pull-repeat striking mechanism disappeared; it would linger on until the advantage of instant illumination was enjoyed by all, but from this period onwards, its main purpose was decorative rather than functional. Also, development of the balance-wheel escapement, especially as applied to marine chronometers, had been proceeding apace over the last hundred years, and by 1840 it was possible to purchase, quite economically, a clock (or watch) that would be as accurate a timekeeper as the pendulum clock. The bracket clock would now remain, more or less, in one room, while in the bedroom people would tell the time from either a smaller balance-wheel time-piece or the owner's watch hung in a holder on the bedpost. In fact, balance-wheel clocks were made in sizes up to that of the bracket clock, which, in any case was shrinking (and would continue to do so for several years).

These small balance-wheel clocks were competing in two markets—for fixed and portable timekeepers. The larger versions, usually by English makers, were making inroads into the pendulum bracket-clock market, and, being up to 12in tall were obviously intended to be fixtures. The smaller versions, say up to 8in tall, were useful as portable clocks and were direct competitors of the French mantel clocks of the period. There is little doubt that these smaller clocks eventually evolved into the brass-cased carriage clock that is now so familiar; but although the brass carriage clock, with its leather carrying-case, was eminently practical, for an aesthetically pleasing clock one cannot match these wooden-cased versions. Ultimately, of course, the French makers dominated the carriage-clock market, with their superior application of mass-production methods. The John Barwise mentioned as a client of Thwaites and Reed was, for a while, chairman of the British Watch Company, an association formed to exploit the production techniques of foreign watchmakers; Sir John Bennet was to advocate a similar campaign later in the nineteenth century, but like most attempts to assault the bastion of British craftsmanship (in those particular fields), both plans failed.

A typical clock of this period is shown in photograph 17. This is by Benjamin Louis Vulliamy about whom there will be further discussion. The clock stands 12in high and was made around 1838–40. Its case is

17 Clock by Benjamin Vulliamy, c1840

veneered in rosewood, very popular for these clocks, and is a simple version of the chamfer top. From the clocks I have seen, the chamfer top seems to have predominated in these clocks—the architectural top, a seventeenth-century style, also made a brief return. There is no embellishment whatever on this case—even the feet are simple wooden forms—and except that the well-figured grain of the rosewood is used to best effect, it would seem sombre indeed. One point to note is the return of the glass side panels, a feature not seen since the last quarter of the eighteenth century.

The dial is a mixture of styles, combining a simple legible Regency dial, silvered on a brass base, and engraving, which has not been seen on a dial for many years. The hands are straight Breguet moon-and-poise, a type that harmonises well with a circular dial and one that would be continued in the majority of carriage clocks. An unusual feature on an English clock is the pendulum rise-and-fall adjustment, situated in the centre of the numeral XII. Rise-and-fall (or 'up-and-down') work is, of course, not new to us, but the English makers had tended to favour the pointer-operating-a-cam system; the type shown here was of French origin, usually attributed to Achille Brocot, who is said to have designed the first suspension adjustment of this type in about 1815. (Members of the Brocot family also patented a perpetual-calendar device and the 'visible' escapement.) The projection through the dial is a small, square-ended rod, turned by a watch-key, which drives a right-angle gear, fixed to the back plate, to transfer the movement into an up-and-down motion; attached to the driven gear is the pendulum suspension strip, passing between fixed cheeks.

The movement of the Vulliamy clock (not illustrated) is a substantial piece of engineering with double-fusee drive, recoil escapement and a heavy lenticular-bob pendulum; the pendulum rod is made of ebony, an extremely dense wood, with a low coefficient of expansion and therefore often used instead of the temperature-compensation devices of the more expensive grid-iron or mercury type. The back plate of the movement is numbered and signed Vulliamy, London; because of the unusual features of rise-and-fall work, ebony pendulum rod and a extremely substantial movement, it is likely that this movement was indeed produced by Vulliamy and not by a jobbing workshop.

The strike hammer on this example operates on a gong, instead of the usual bell. These gongs, made from steel strip coiled into a circular form, had been in limited use from about 1830, but following the completion of the Great Clock of Westminster in 1837 they achieved instant popularity, since their cathedral-like tone is more reminiscent of a church bell than is the rather strident tone of the bracket-clock bell.

By 1835 the population of the United Kingdom, was 19 million, a vast market which, as we have seen was already being exploited successfully by French, German and Austrian clockmakers; the distribution of wealth was more uneven than possibly it had ever been, ranging from the riches of the successful land or factory owner down to abject poverty level. Only three years had passed since the Loveless Brothers (the 'Tolpuddle Martyrs') had been shipped off to the penal colony in Australia as a result of their attempt to gain better working conditions. A parlour maid might earn £12 a year and a skilled machine operator would be earning about £2 a week; Thwaites and Reed were paying their skilled clockmakers around £1 15s a week.

Looking, then, at the purchase price of clocks, we can get some idea of what the clocks were and the markets for which they were intended. Turner of Fenchurch Street, London, is listed in the directories as a watchmaker, clockmaker and jeweller; a record exists of his stock at one particular period, during 1834. The clock section is as follows:

ITEM	PURCHASE PRICE
Gothic timepiece, rosewood, 8-day	£12 12s 0d
Rosewood, ——— top, striking	£14 0s 0d
12″ dial, convex	£6 6s 0d
12″ dial	£5 5s 0d
Rosewood bracket clock, striking on gong	£13 10s 0d
French Gothic, gilt, striking, under shade	£16 16s 0d
Small rosewood, 8-day timepiece, square, silver dial	£10 0s 0d
Mahogany, double claw bracket	£1 8s 0d
Carved mahogany bracket	£1 0s 0d

Several interesting points arise from this list. The first is that of the three bracket clocks (all new stock), not one had a matching bracket; in fact, a perusal of Turner's sales indicates that he sold some thirty bracket clocks during the year, and only one of them was listed as having a wall bracket. The 'double claw' bracket in the list could have been one that matched the claw feet of some Regency bracket clocks.

It seems likely that the small rosewood timepiece, with its silvered dial, was of a similar type to the Vulliamy clock, and even this, at a price of £10, would be out of the range available to the artisan. A 12in dial clock would cost him about a month's wages; if this was beyond reach, he would have to satisfy himself with a foreign wall clock (perhaps a cuckoo-clock), or rely on one of the increasing number of public and private turret clocks.

PUBLIC CLOCKS—BENJAMIN VULLIAMY

This was a market that several English clockmakers entered from 1830 onwards and the records of Thwaites and Reeds show an increasing amount of turret-clock work, to the detriment of spring-clock sales. This area at least was one where the English makers would predominate, and was perhaps a reason why such competition in bracket clocks was allowed to develop, and why the English are now world-renowned for public clocks, with the firms of Elliotts, Dent, Gillet and Johnson, Thwaites and Reed (now Elliott) being household names in that field.

The mention of turret clocks is relevant to this period, especially in the interaction of Dents and Benjamin Vulliamy, as it saw the building of probably the most famous turret clock in the world, London's Great Clock of Westminster, the chimes of which would be copied by countless thousands of bracket clocks and mantel clocks from its completion in 1837 to the present day. In 1834, following the loss by fire of the Palace of Westminster, the designer Charles Barry was successful in his proposal to build a new tower; this was supposedly in the Gothic style (still in favour at that time, when Penrhyn Castle was under way), although the term 'Gothic' is applied loosely to this design. Barry wrote to Vulliamy, who was then Master of the Clockmakers Company, requesting a plan for the clock, and Vulliamy suggested one of his own designs; however the Astronomer Royal, George Airey, favoured the work of Edward John Dent, who had recently completed a clock for the Royal Exchange and who was by then a renowned maker of chronometers. John Whitehurst of Derby, another well-known maker suggested that the clock should be powered by that recent novelty electricity. It was decided that a public competition would be held, but as Whitehurst's electrically powered clock was rejected, and Vulliamy refused to submit himself to open competition, the field was left clear for Dent. The rest of the story is interspersed with disasters and personality clashes between Airey, Barry, Dent, Rippon (Dent's successor, since Dent died during the saga) and E. B. Denison, the inventor of the double three-legged gravity escapement used in this clock; it is not a story for this book but the incident serves to illustrate the character of the top clockmakers of that period, of whom Vulliamy was probably the most enigmatic—if that word is diplomatic enough.

During his attempts to secure the contract for the clock of Westminster, Vulliamy made a working model of his design; having refused to compete with the other tenderers, he sold the clock to Sir Morton Peto, the owner of Somerleyton Hall, Norfolk. A tower was built in the stable block to house it and (although the movement is not available for viewing) it can be seen today, apparently in good working order. (Somerleyton Hall is now the family seat of the Crossleys.)

One of Vulliamy's major contributions to English clock development seems to have been a propensity for ripping out movements by early English clockmakers, dismissing them as poor workmanship and substituting a movement of his own making. This act was perpetrated on a number of clocks, including a grand-sonnerie bracket-clock movement by Tompion, which he did retain and present to the Institution of Civil Engineers. However, to show the other side of the coin, S. Benson Beeves, in his biography of Vulliamy, explains that such drastic modifications to important old clocks were made at a time when antiquarian horology did not exist, in its present sense, and were in the eyes of that period not nearly as reprehensible as they now appear. It is also true that Vulliamy was a fine clockmaker in his own right. With his death, in 1855, the last of the individualists had gone and from now on the *company* would rule the bracket-clock scene.

7

CONSOLIDATION AND COMPETITION
1850–1900

Most people, asked which clock typified the solid middle-class respect-ability of the Victorian period, would reply 'The black marble clock'. This would be not far from the truth, if only for the fact that so many of these clocks seem to have been made that there were not enough people to buy them! The clocks provided keen competition to all others in the lower end of the market, but although, as we shall see, they made some incursions into the bracket-clock market they did not become a serious threat there. The top 10–20 per cent of the population were still potential customers for the bracket-clock makers.

Bracket clocks grew if anything larger during this period, and towards the end of the century appeared, lemming-like, to be going the way of the white-dial longcase, growing to proportions that edged into down-right ugliness. But that was not yet. If anything typified the bracket clock at the beginning of this period, it was the mahogany or rosewood case with applied carving—nothing elaborate or even elegant, but solid engineering.

A clock dating from 1850–60, by Ramsey of Devonport, is shown in photographs 18 and 19. It stands 18in high, and is 13in wide and 9in deep. The case style is indeterminate—no new case styles evolved during the period 1850–1900—but could be described as 'leaning towards' the Gothic in general outline. Most of the English cases of this period follow the basically simple decoration in a mixture of styles, ranging from the true Gothic, through the full-arch, elaborated arch and break-arch, without settling into one definitive style.

The case in this particular example is in rosewood veneer, with applied carving of a floral motif; it is taller than the average Regency clock of forty years previously, because of a lengthened lower apron, upon which is additional carving. On some later clocks, this lower apron increased to such proportions that the whole design was thrown out of balance, but here it is quite pleasing, giving the clock an apparent 'bombe' base, in Louis XV style. The 'cheese' feet are of wood, but unlike the more severe style of the 1840s, the clock now sports a pair of brass handles—these are to be considered as for decorative purposes only

18 Clock by Ramsey of Devonport, c1855

19 Rear view of Ramsey clock

(beginners please note!) as this clock is too heavy to be readily portable. The handles may have been functional when the clock was new, but age and fatigue will have their way, as the number of handle-less and broken cases will testify.

The dial is convex, of painted iron, bearing the legend 'E Ramsey, Devonport' and probably in original condition; the hands are an elaborate form of the Gothic trefoil, more correctly I suppose to be termed quatrefoil. Whatever the terminology, they are a pleasing form of what by now was very much a mass-produced item.

Inside the case (and just visible, to the right of the pendulum-bob) is a retailer's label bearing the name R. Hoeler, of 23 Marlborough St, Devonport; this label also carries a repair date of 1886, with a price of 3/6d, and the initials R.D. Underneath the case is a scratched-in name which appears to be Rev R. S. Hawks, with a date of 1850—so already we have the confusion of three names on the clock.

The movement is a standard twin-fusee drive with a plain backplate, looking like the product of a jobbing workshop; however, there are no telltale signs or numbers in the usual places, such as under the bracket, inside the bell, under the bell stand, on the pendulum or on the plates. There may be a maker's mark on the inside of one of the spring barrels, but this would only be revealed by dismantling the movement.

An interesting point about the movement is that there is provision for a pull-repeat mechanism; the star wheel and click are fitted, as is the lifting lever, but the actual cord and button are missing. What is *not* fitted is a strike/silent device, which infers that the pull-repeat is for decorative purposes only (unusual in a mid-Victorian clock), since no one in their right mind would consider taking a bracket clock, with its strident bell that cannot be silenced, up to the bedroom. One explanation could lie in the fact that the lifting lever, for the strike train, has an extended arbor to the front plate: it could perhaps have been fitted with a strike/silent device as an 'optional extra'. The fact that it was not lends weight to the theory that the movement was supplied by a London workshop, ready for the clockmaker/retailer to add the refinements.

A further point is that the dial was not originally fitted to the movement. The dial has the usual feet for fitting directly to the front plate of a movement, since the distance between the shoulder on the dial foot and the hole through which the securing pin would be fitted correspond, approximately, to the thickness of the normal front plate—as we would expect. Here a false plate has been fitted, similar to those used in white-dial longcase clocks, and a second set of holes has been drilled in the dial feet to accommodate the thinner metal of the false plate. This conversion, if it can be termed such, is no recent event—if it was not carried out when the clock was first assembled, then it was done very shortly afterwards. It is possible that Mr Ramsey of Devonport already had a dial, and possibly a case as well, in stock, and used a false plate to attach this to a bought-in movement.

Overall, the clock is a pleasant and solid example of early Victorian clockmaking. Furniture, in the early Victorian period, was of solid form—as with the clocks, applied decoration or carving was the norm and acanthus leaves sprouted everywhere; the Victorian passion for carving spilled over into applying it to earlier furniture, and many a travelling chest from the seventeenth century or longcase from the eighteenth century has suffered the ignominy of a change in taste. Furniture in particular moved away drastically from the Sheraton/Empire elegance of the Regency period and developed overtones of Gothic and Elizabethan. This could have been due to the arrival of a dominant but dour queen, or the aftermath of England's financial problems, or the age of the engineer and its influence on design. Around 1875 however the trend began to reverse, with an interest in the days of past splendours, a hankering after the dream, if not the reality, of the Sheraton, Chippendale, Hepplewhite and Adam styles.

Until this time, British taste in design had not suited the French manufacturers, who after all were the only serious competitors in the bracket-clock field. Their second Empire, and later developments, had resulted in a style that was far too ornate for the English taste, but once the revival began they were well equipped to take advantage, unlike all but a handful of the English makers. The main thrust was not a direct assault on the traditional style of the bracket clock (that would come later, with the arrival of the German firms), but on the sites that the bracket clock held—the hall, the dining-room sideboard, the with-drawing-room, etc. During the period 1875–90, therefore, we saw two styles of architecture and furniture running in parallel, the Gothic in its various forms (lancet, Romanesque, perpendicular and Tudor) and the Classical (mainly Adam, but with traces of Sheraton and Hepplewhite). The Gothic was on the wane by 1890, when the Classical took over, running through the Edwardian period and into the 1920s.

Gothic-style architecture and furniture were of course heavy and sombre, consistent with the image of middle-class respectability in the mid-Victorian period. The French 'marble' clock, as well as the rosewood English bracket clock, suited this setting, as did the type of clock similar to that by Ramsey (photograph 18), but larger and more elaborate bracket clocks were entering the upper end of the market. These no longer had an individual style, but used previous designs, often with several styles brought together in the same clock. They were destined for company boardrooms and public buildings, or perhaps became hall centre-pieces in grander residences. Where expense was no object, they would be fitted with three-train movements, the third train driving a chime mechanism, which would almost inevitably include a reproduction of the chimes of the great clock of Westminster. (Since chiming clocks appeared in ever-increasing numbers after about 1860, a separate section deals with this feature at the end of this chapter.)

A typical large bracket clock from the period 1875–85 is shown in photograph 20. This was made by A. & H. Rowley, of Grays Inn Road, London, and stands over 20in high to the terminal—a magnificent specimen. The case is basically of the break-arch design, the break arch being supported by columns with brass capitals. The feet, again in brass, are similar in design to those used in the clocks of the French First and Second Empire period and are an overt symbol of the quality of manufacture in this clock. The arch is no longer a simple form and, indeed, it would be difficult to find a clock of this period without top ornamentation—most of the expensive bracket clocks seemed to follow the elaborate (if not over-elaborate) Hope design, adding upper-works to both the arch and the Gothic styles. The terminal, in the form of an urn, is again a quality casting. The case material is oak veneer, the designer relying on external decoration rather than the natural beauty of a more exotic wood; but many of these clocks were made with the hardwood veneers popular at this period—mahogany and rosewood.

The dial is of the full-arch type, developed earlier in the century, with a silvered chapter ring and matted centre; the spandrels, in a rococo style, fill the spaces of the dial and the strike/silent lever (or, in this case, chime/silent) is fitted neatly into the arch. The hands are mass-produced, but are a pleasant version of the serpentine form developed in the 1750s. We have, therefore, a mixture of styles—a case form from 1790, the Hope additions from about 1810, the full-arch dial from about 1820, the hands and spandrels from the eighteenth century—but they can, as here, add up to an attractive whole.

The movement is three-train, going, striking and chiming, each train having its own fusee drive and is probably English-made; its construction can only be described as massive—it looks as though it will still be functioning in another hundred years. As one author put it, some of these movements from the large bracket clocks of the period would not be out of place in the engine room of the *Great Eastern*. They were made for a market where cost was no object; the French and others could compete in the middle-to-lower end of the market, but the English makers, with their traditional design, could as yet hold their own in this particular sector.

20 Large bracket clock by Rowley, London, c1875

A. & H. Rowley were trading as clockmakers throughout most of the nineteenth century. At the International Inventors' Exhibition of 1885 they had included in a display of their work a large chiming clock, with a perpetual calendar and automata, and a clock with 'improved' chiming on bells and gongs in a 'Gothic' oak case. (The clock in the illustration would probably be called 'Gothic' at that time.)

THE FRENCH CLOCKS

The cheaper range of the market was, as mentioned, supplied mainly by the plain English bracket clock, in competition with the better-quality French 'marble' clocks. These French clocks were not in fact made from marble but from limestone, the main source of this being the Ardennes district of Belgium. For the majority of cases, the limestone is 'veneered' to a carcase of fine cement, composed of a mixture of Russian tallow, resin and brick dust. The larger cases had steel reinforcement rods keyed into the cement, and since some of these cases weigh upwards of 20 kilos, reinforcement is necessary. The more expensive and intricate cases might be machined from solid limestone, with bandings or inlays of 'real' marble or onyx. In general this type of clock did not compete with the traditional English bracket clock. Nevertheless, there are several examples remaining which are so close to the bracket-clock style that they must have provided direct competition, especially on a price comparison; whereas a typical English bracket clock of about 1880 would cost around £20, the marble clock of similar size would be in the £5–£10 range.

A French clock of this type, made about 1880, is shown in photograph 21; the clock stands 13in high to the terminal, and is 9in wide, 5in deep. The case is of limestone, which when polished is black (if these cases are neglected, they often revert to their natural, unpolished grey colour), the limestone being a 6mm 'veneer' on a cement carcase. This particular carcase has the metal reinforcing rods bedded in to the cement—larger examples have rods passing through the carcase with screwed ends carrying nuts and washers to stiffen up the frame. On the front apron, the limestone has been engraved with a symmetrical floral design, the incised area being filled with a gilt enamel paint; the vertical banding is in brown marble.

The general case form is that of the chamfer top, the terminal in this example being in the more usual French flambeau design, as distinct from the English pineapple; the terminal is cast metal, with a spun-metal apron, gilded after manufacture—the finish is not original and it is likely that originally the terminal was gold-leafed, with a shellac protective coat. The feet are brass, in a caddy-ball form, and the handles, on the side of the case, are in cast brass; these lion-head handles are much more elaborate and stylised than those of the English Regency period and are definitely for decoration only.

The brass bezel has the common French-style dentil moulding to the sight ring, with a stove-enamelled dial behind it; French makers, almost without exception, used a stove-enamelled dial on all the clocks of this

21 French bracket clock, c1880

type, resulting in a purer depth of colour. The major problem is that if the dial is damaged, repair is exceedingly difficult, in comparison with repainting an English dial. This particular dial has a floral design in the centre, with fleur-de-lys motifs between the minute markings. The hands are also in fleur-de-lys form (illustrated in figure 31), a style to be favoured increasingly towards the end of the nineteenth century; the fleur-de-lys was the heraldic symbol of the French kings, similar in form to the 'three feathers' symbol of the Prince of Wales.

Figure 31 Fleur-de-lys hands

Above the numeral XII on the dial can be seen the small arbor of the Brocot suspension adjustment fitted to the movement. The movement is the usual 'roulant' type, two 80mm diameter plates separated by three pillars. The drive is by spring barrels only—no fusees here—containing long, light springs giving about fourteen days' drive to the clock. As usual with these clocks all the movement parts are finely finished, with slender arbors, delicate wheels and solid pinions. The strike train, with hours and half-hours on a bell, is of the countwheel type, a feature which persisted in French clocks until the end of the nineteenth century, probably because it was cheap to produce and gave good service when the clock was new. In an old clock, however, the countwheel strike tends to be somewhat temperamental about counting consistently.

The movement is a mass-produced one, with no indication of the actual manufacturer, except for the serial number, 1467, stamped into the back plate. At the bottom of the back plate are the numbers 52, this to be read as 5.2 French 'inches' (1 French 'inch' = 1.06 British inches, for practical purposes the same length), denoting the pendulum length; a similar number is usually stamped on the pendulum-bob and this is a useful feature if one comes across a clock minus its pendulum.

The bell strike is an interesting feature. Nowadays, of course, the bell-strike clock is very acceptable, although the bell itself would cost more to produce than a coiled-tape gong; but in 1880 the reverse was true—a gong would cost more than a bell. So the majority of French clocks had bells, which were cast in vast numbers, usually in a bronze alloy.

The French had been mass-producing these 'roulant' movements for many years, the most prolific manufacturer being the Japy Brothers; they developed the circular form of the movement from the square-plate movement of the late eighteenth century, producing in the main the *roulants blancs*, the two plates, with the pillars and the going barrel fitted, to which the clockmaker could add the refinements. If you should chance upon one of their movements, the form of the company logo may be an aid to dating the clock. From 1837 onwards, the movements were stamped simply 'Japy Frères', but from 1854 onwards this became 'Japy Frères et Cie'; in 1928, the company 'went public', becoming 'Société Anonyme des Etablissements Japy Frères'. In the Great Exhibition of 1855, the company was awarded a Grande Médaille d'Honneur for producing 60,000 *roulants blancs* in one year, a measure of the volume coming from just one (admittedly, the most prolific) manufacturer, many of whose products were destined for eventual export to England. From 1855 onwards, a note that they had been presented with this award appears on their movements.

As we move into the last quarter of the nineteenth century, the French were not in serious competition in the bracket-clock market. It is true that they sold, in large numbers, a scaled-down and cheapened version of the waisted bracket clock, one that stood about 12in high, with the boulle inlay of the earlier clocks now replaced by machine-made decoration; but these were mostly designed to compete with the smaller bracket clocks. For example, a fairly average boulle-type clock, with little or no decoration but lots of cast brass, standing between 10 and 16 inches high, would cost between £6 and £16 by 1890. Compare this with a timepiece carriage clock at £3 10s, or one with hour and half-hour striking at around £8–£10, when an English bracket clock would cost over £25, and one can see that these clocks were not a serious threat to the bracket-clock makers; they were aimed at the ever-increasing middle market, where mass-production methods could satisfy consumer demand.

Both American and German manufacturers had been importing clocks into Britain through agents in ever-increasing numbers during the nineteenth century. Such American makers as Ansonia, Seth Thomas, the New Haven Clock Co, the Waterbury Clock Co, William Gilbert and E. N. Welch were household names by 1875, dominating the scene with their cheap mass-produced clocks, doing just what the British had been exhorted to do in the early years of the century; but they made only rare incursions into the bracket-clock field. Those that did soon enter this domain were the Germans Winterhalder and Hofmeyer, HAC and Lenzkirch, with to a minor degree the firm of Junghans.

The Germans had of course been producing clocks since the dawn of clockmaking, but had tended to keep to specialised handwork; this was changed in the latter half of the nineteenth century. Some of the Junghans family actually worked for a while in America, learning the techniques of mass production, and then applied them at home. A superficial glance at, for instance, a shelf or mantel clock of the late nineteenth century will not reveal its provenance—it could be either German or American, for the origins were the same; even the name is often confusing—the full title of HAC, for instance, is the Hamburg

America Clock Co! The German makers did not stop at producing mantel clocks; their background enabled them to apply mass-production methods to the manufacture of robust movements, including a few fusee types, and this is where they could compete with the English makers.

We can illustrate the effect of this competition by studying the clock shown in photograph 22; this particular example was manufactured around 1890–1900, and stands 16in high, 11in wide. The case is in rosewood, still a very popular veneer in the English market, and is of the break-arch style, elaborated with a pineapple terminal; the terminal, the pineapple finials, the feet and the caryatids supporting the break arch are all of cast brass and of good definition. The case has arched panels to the side and a full-width front door, with a sight 'ring' or dial mask of steel, copper-coated and silvered, a visual feature of this type of clock.

The dial has a silvered chapter ring, with good-quality spandrels, the arch containing the lever for the pendulum up-and-down work, a feature not seen in any quantity since the eighteenth century. The hands are of blued steel (or, more correctly, 'blacked' steel) and are of the by now commonly used fleur-de-lys design. Overall a pleasant clock, which *could* be English made, except for the hands, which *should* be of French origin.

However, a study of the movement, photograph 23, reveals a definitely un-English appearance. This movement, in fact, was made by Winterhalder and Hofmeyer, Schwerzenbach, as evidenced by the logo 'W. & H. Sch.' stamped on the backplate. The drive is two-train, using springs in barrels, without fusees, the wheelwork and general finish being of good quality. The cheaper German (and American) clocks used 'lantern' pinions (so-called because of their resemblance to a cage lantern), consisting of steel rollers, instead of pinion leaves, fixed between two brass circular plates. But W. & H., amongst others, usually employed solid pinions, as here, in their more expensive clocks. The pendulum up-and-down work can be seen clearly in this illustration, and this device was to be a regular feature in such clocks over the next twenty years; one cynic has suggested that they had to have a convenient method of adjusting the pendulum length, because their timekeeping qualities were notoriously inaccurate, but this is overstating the case. I have owned, or known, many such movements and have never found their timekeeping a problem.

The chime system is of interest, since it is of the earliest type, the 'ting-tang'. We have already seen this system in use in the eighteenth century, on for example the clock by John Rayment, but it tended to fall from favour during the Regency period. The German manufacturers revived it, using coiled-tape gongs, instead of the earlier bells, and it was frequently used during the period 1875–1920. One of its advantages was

22 Clock by Winterhalder
& Hofmeyer, c1890

23 Back of Winterhalder & Hofmeyer
clock, revealing coiled-tape gongs

that, being a simple chime, it did not require as much spring power as a more complicated chime and could be driven from the strike train; so the clock offered the bonus of a chime with the economy of a two-train movement whereas a full chime sequence would necessitate a third driving train if it was to be in continual use. (Remember that in the earlier full-chime, two-train movements, the chime operated on a pull-repeat only, and not as a continual operation.) On this example, the same hammers sound the quarters and the hours; but as the hour approaches one hammer is lifted clear of the gong by a peg and 'feathers', while the other hammer sounds the hour on the deeper-toned gong. One problem of ageing with such clocks is that towards the end of the normal eight-day going period, when the spring is 'tired', the chiming sequence can sound somewhat funereal.

The escapement is of the recoil, or anchor, type, driving a lenticular-bob pendulum much lighter in weight than the type used with a fusee system. A further point to note is the liberal use of screwed joints, especially in the pillar-to-backplate fixings, a feature the Germans used with great success.

By 1891 most families could afford a clock of some kind, and the population of the United Kingdom had risen to 34 million—to be 38 million by 1901. At the cheaper end of the market most of the clocks bought were German, American or French. Examples of English clocks in this range are few. During the period 1890–1900 the only type to sell in quantity was the wall dial clock, and even that faced heavy competition from the American dropdial clocks and German 'Vienna regulator' wall clocks. English makers had tended to diversify, and while it was possible to have a one-off bracket clock made by Elliott's, Dent or Thwaites and Reed, the top names in clock-making had turned to newer fields, where foreign competition was inferior or absent—as with turret clocks or chronometers. Occasionally one finds an English-cased German movement, but on the whole the German makers had the bracket-clock field to themselves by 1900. With the increase in population and wealth, the bracket clock made by mass-production methods was now available to the middle classes—shopkeepers, office managers, local government officials and the like. The upper classes, and the institutional buyers, could be left to the individuality of the English makers, being the few who could afford traditional quality.

One feature that was common to the range of bracket clocks during the late nineteenth century was the chiming mechanism. I dealt at some length with the building of a turret clock, the great clock of Westminster, because in the years following this, domestic clocks with chimes that imitated it became immensely popular.

CHIMES IN BRACKET CLOCKS

Chiming clocks were in fact at their most popular during the period 1880–1930. As mentioned earlier, the simplest and earliest chime is the two-note 'ting-tang'. It is not known for certain when and where this chime was first used. Originally it used a half-note interval, sounding the hour on a third bell pitched one tone lower. The original version of the chime may still be heard in some country churches and in the colleges of some of the older universities. It is a chime that fits well with the solitary authority of a church tower—but it does not transfer too happily to a domestic clock and a smaller set of bells. The version used in bracket clocks, from the seventeenth century onwards, used a 'smoother' interval of a harmonic third, and to save having a third bell for the hour this was struck on the lower-toned of the two bells only.

Figure 32 'Ting-tang' chime

Figure 33 The smoother version of the 'ting-tang' chime

The advantage, as I said, of this chime is that it is just possible to serve the chime and the hour strike with one driving train—this is *always* done with late nineteenth-century German clocks. A further advantage is that the mechanism required to operate the chime may be a simple single wheel, the single lifting lever raising each hammer in turn; the hour rack is used for sounding the quarters, the drop of the rack being controlled by a cam.

A chime of more than two notes becomes more complicated. The usual method was to use a pinned barrel in the fashion of a musical-box; in rotating it lifted the hammers in a sequence depending on the position of the pins. This is shown diagrammatically in figure 34. The barrel pins are fixed, of course, and can only perform a set sequence, but it is possible

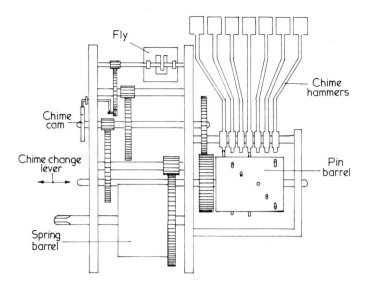

Figure 34 German chime train with pinned barrel

to arrange a further set of pins, offset axially on the barrel. If the barrel itself can be made to slide axially, as well as rotating, then different sets of pins, to play different melodies, can be brought into contact with the hammer tails. This, again, is the principle on which the four, six and eight air musical-box works. However, as an air, or chime, usually consists of several notes, it is not often possible to drive the barrel and the hour strike on a single train; this can only be done if the chime is intermittent, for example with a pull-repeat system; even then, continual use of the chime will quickly lower the strength of a single spring. This is one reason why the earlier makers, as I have illustrated, preferred to have the chime side as a separate pull wind—pulling the pull-repeat cord wound up a small spring capable of driving the chime barrel for the duration of one chime.

For clocks designed to have the chimes in continual use, a third train is usually necessary; the clock by A. & H. Rowley (see photograph 20) is an example, although the third winding-hole is a little difficult to see, being hidden behind the hour hand.

Chiming clocks of the eighteenth and nineteenth centuries used the rack chiming system. This is similar in operation to the rack striking system (see figure 10). The counting of the correct chime period is achieved by a gathering pallet picking up the teeth of a rack; the rack falls to a four-step snail fitted to the motion work between the hour snail and the front plate. A typical arrangement for rack chiming is shown in figure 35. This system was sometimes fitted with a pull-repeat, since like the rack strike it will always sound the correct quarter. It was an expensive device, because not only was there a third train but the extra motion work, rack, lifting-pieces, gathering pallet and various levers to co-ordinate the operation had to be made and fitted. A three-train rack chiming movement, complete and ready to fit, was the most expensive standard movement for a bracket clock.

Once the Germans ventured into the chiming-clock market, however, they developed a countwheel system of chiming that was much cheaper than the rack; English makers copied this for the middle-market range of clocks, retaining the rack system for very expensive clocks, such as the

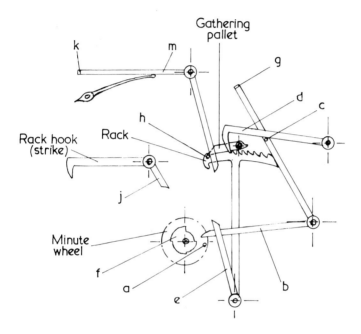

Figure 35   Rack chiming mechanism. The minute wheel is fitted with four pins to correspond with the four quarter hours. At the quarter, pin 'a' raises the lifting piece 'b', pin 'c' on the lifting piece raising the rack hook 'd'; the rack tail 'e' then falls to the relevant stop on the four-step snail 'f'. The train runs, but is arrested by the projection 'g', on the lifting piece, contacting a stop pin on the striking train (not shown); the train is now at the warning stage. At the quarter, the lifting piece 'b' is released by pin 'a' and projection 'g' falls away from the warning stop pin; the train now runs, as the gathering pallet picks up the rack teeth. Once the gathering pallet contacts the stop pin 'h' on the rack, the train is arrested. As the hour approaches the geometry is such that the rack, in falling to the lowest stop on the cam 'f', contacts the rack hook tail 'j', on the strike train rack, so that the strike train also runs to its warning stop pin; lever 'm' is released as the chime rack falls and, under spring assistance, has raised projection 'h' to a point where it will contact the warning stop pin on the strike train. At the hour, the chime train will run, as before, but the strike train will be held on warning until all chime rack teeth have been gathered—at this point, the chime rack will move lever 'm', projection 'k' will fall away from the warning stop pin and the strike train will run.

one by Rowley. There are many forms of the basic countwheel chime system, most involving the release of the strike train by the chime levers at the end of the fourth quarter. A typical system is shown in figure 36. Some nineteenth-century German movements had the strike train released independently.

The usual layout for the three trains, looking at the clock from the front, is that the hour-strike train is on the left, the going train in the centre and the chime train on the right; all the German factory-made movements use this layout. Having three trains presents problems not only in the manufacture of the movement but in the aesthetic appearance of the dial; because of the spacing necessary to fit three spring barrels, in smaller clocks the winding arbors would project through the dial in the middle of the chapter ring—an unappealing prospect. Some German

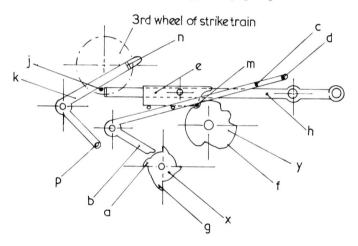

Figure 36   Arrangement of lifting levers for chime and hour strike.

For quarter striking, the low lift 'a' on wheel 'x' lifts lever 'b'. This unlocks the chiming train by lifting the stop 'd' from the pin on the 3rd wheel, this pin rotating a half revolution until arrested by stop 'c'. Lever 'b' also lifts the pivoting part, 'e', of lever 'h' to clear pin 'm' from the cam slot. As the cam 'a' releases lever 'b', stop 'c' falls away from the pin, allowing the train to run for a period determined by the length of land of cam 'y'.

For hour striking, the high lift 'g' on wheel 'x' lifts lever 'b', as before, to set and run the chime train; being a high lift, it also raises lever 'h', which, in turn, lifts lever 'k'. Lever 'k' releases the stop 'n', on the strike train and the 3rd wheel rotates until it is arrested by the stop 'j', on lever 'h'. Whilst the chime train is running, lever 'h' remains lifted by the higher lift cam, 'f', on wheel 'y' on which pin 'm' is riding. Once the chime train has completed its sequence, pin 'm' drops into the next valley in the cam, lowering lever 'h' and allowing the strike train to operate. Lever 'k', during this time, is held raised by the pin 'p' which has engaged with the teeth of the strike rack (not shown). Once striking is completed, pin 'p' drops beneath the strike rack, allowing lever 'k' to drop, locking off the strike train at stop 'n'.

clocks circumvent this by winding the spring barrels through an intermediate set of gears, enabling the winding 'arbors' to be fitted to the front plate only, connected to the true arbors through a gear wheel. The winding arbors can then be close enough together for all three to be placed within the chapter ring; a clock of this type is illustrated later, photograph 28. On larger clocks, such as the one by Rowley, it is just possible to site the winding arbors, directly connect to the spring barrels (or in this case the fusee spindles), within the chapter ring—although, as here, they have to be moved to its extreme edge.

Once a third train and chime barrel are fitted, the only limitations on the chime are the number of notes within the chime (therefore the number of bells to be fitted) and the duration of the chime; after all, the chime-train spring must be strong enough to perform for eight days to match the normal going period of the clock. A further problem arises with the 'speed' of the chime—not the rotation of the barrel, which will be fixed in any case, but the number of individual notes to be struck in the time period. The illustration of the chime barrel shows that the system is relatively slow-acting, since the pin is in contact with the hammer tail for a considerable time. It would be impossible, for instance, for this system to play the first bar of the Warsaw Concerto: it would have to use a single hammer, lifted three times in rapid succession by three pins aligned circumferentially around the barrel—the second and third pins would be moving into position while the first pin was still lifting the hammer tail. For this reason a movement designed to play a march or a folk dance (as some of the early, and expensive, bracket clocks were) will often have more hammers than bells. It will be arranged so that if one note has to sound successively, one hammer tail will be on the point of release while the second hammer tail is already being lifted, the two then being able to strike the same bell in rapid succession. This does give an odd appearance to the hammers—the bells will normally be nested (fitted inside each other, with spacers, to take less room) and therefore quite close together, but the hammers must be strung out along their arbor; and a second hammer striking the same bell has to be bent out of line to be within striking distance of the bell. So it may look a bit messy, but that is the design.

Throughout the seventeenth and eighteenth centuries, the chime was always on cast metal bells, the only available device producing a reasonable sound when struck with a hammer; it was pleasant for a light air, but could not successfully imitate the sombre, rounded tone of a tower bell. In the early part of the nineteenth century, around 1820–30, the coiled-tape gong was introduced (figure 37) and was immediately successful, since its tone, when hit with a soft hammer, was far nearer

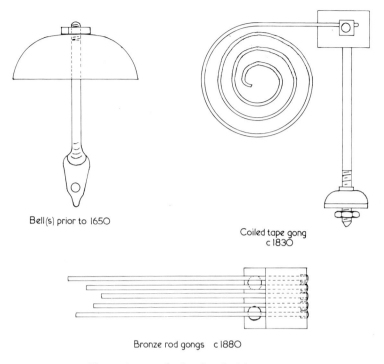

Bell(s) prior to 1650

Coiled tape gong
c 1830

Bronze rod gongs   c 1880

Figure 37   Methods of strike/chime

that of a tower bell than could be achieved with any small bell struck with a solid hammer. Some early clocks using a solid metal hammer give a distinctive metallic sound, very like the chimes often used in continental church towers. Clocks using a solid hammer with a leather insert give a fuller, heavier sound, similar to that of English church-clock chimes, especially those built after 1850. In the nineteenth century, a coiled-tape gong was more expensive to produce than a cast bell, since although the foundries were geared up to producing small castings for clock parts, they were unused to metal forming of this type; the coil tape needed to be heated and then coiled around a mandrel, each gong needing individual treatment, as against the batch-casting of several bells. The reverse would be true today; coiled-tape gongs can be produced by cold forming on an automatic or semi-automatic machine, a technique used by German and American manufacturers in the late nineteenth century. A set of bells, however, is nowadays an expensive item, since the foundries only produce to special order, or the customer has to wait until they have orders for sufficient sets to be worth the casting.

The introduction of volume-production techniques went a long way to account for the coiled-tape gong's popularity, but it owed this even more, in Britain, to the building of that Great Clock of Westminster. I have discussed the problems of the clock itself in an earlier chapter, but these were small compared with the problems of the building of the tower; the clock was finished in 1854 and ran quite happily for five years in the Dent workshop, awaiting the completion of the tower. However, it was installed in 1859, and although critics of the building found it funereal and uninteresting it captured the imagination of the general public. The particular chime chosen was not a new one. In 1793, for the rebuilding of St Mary's Church, Cambridge, a Dr Crotch composed a chime based on one line of the aria from Handel's 'Messiah': 'I know that my Redeemer liveth'. It was known as the Cambridge chime, and was the one chosen for the Westminster clock. I have heard it said that a clock with 'Westminster' chimes made before 1854 must be a fake, but that statement is made in ignorance of the fact that the chime had been in use, under a different name, for sixty years and more. What I have been unable to figure out is an old catalogue picture of an American longcase clock, dating from about 1900, that had the tune selector marked for both Cambridge *and* Westminster chimes!

The chime is based on four notes, with the hour being struck on a fifth bell. As can be seen from the notation (figure 38), the hour-bell note is a bass one—the Westminster clock had a bell of 14 tons to produce this at the required intensity. It is this bell that, by popular belief, should be called 'Big Ben'—reputedly after Sir Benjamin Hall, the Commissioner of Works for the rebuilding, although later the name was applied to the whole clock. Certainly there had never been such national popularity for any chime. It has the advatage of needing only five gongs; it is rarely, if ever, sounded on bells since they do not give the stately sound desired.

Another English church chime occasionally to be found on seventeenth and eighteenth-century clocks is that of the now-demolished Holy

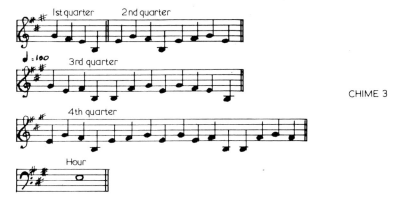

Figure 38   Westminster

Figure 39 Six-bell, Holy Trinity chime

Trinity Church in London. This is a six-bell chime and it sounded better on bells, its 'lightness' being unsuited to gongs. It tended to lose favour at the end of the eighteenth century, and once coiled-tape gongs were introduced it would not have been revived.

German manufacturers introduced a new device for chiming movements in about 1880. This was the rod gong (see figure 37), which had the advantage that it did not need coiling and, being more or less in one plane, could be fitted into a smaller space than the coiled-tape type. The rods were usually of phosphor-bronze, with the more expensive option of nickel silver, and were cut to length, depending on the note required.

Figure 40 St Michael's

This 'tuning' was usually done by hand once the rods were set up rigidly on their mounting block. Rod gongs create a lighter note than the coiled-tape gongs and are therefore suitable for an up-tempo chime, such as the one used in St Michael's Church, Hamburg. This chime was of course more popular with the German manufacturers, but it was also acceptable to the British buying public, coming into general use about 1890–1900.

A third popular chime is the Whittington, but the version so named that appears in chiming clocks is rarely the 'original' eleven-bell Whittington tune from Bow Church, London, itself based on an earlier six-bell tune. The one usually found in German and American clocks is an eight-bell version. This sounds pleasant on rod gongs and especially good on bells. It was the popularity of chimes such as the St Michael's and the Whittington that was probably responsible for the reintroduction of bell sets in the last quarter of the nineteenth century. The bells are not as well cast as their ancestors, some sets in fact being of spun rather than cast metal, but they produce an acceptable sound.

By the end of the nineteenth century, then, we have several options available to the chiming bracket-clock market. At the cheaper end was a

CHIME 6

Figure 41 Eleven-bell Whittington

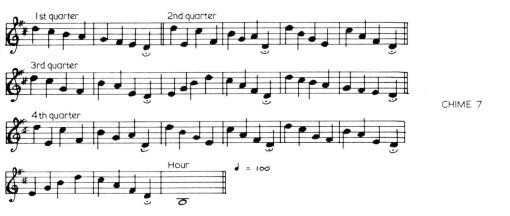

CHIME 7

Figure 42 Eight-bell Whittington

five-rod set of gongs, giving Westminster chimes only on a fixed barrel. A more expensive version would have seven rods and a sliding barrel, giving the alternative of Westminster or Whittington chimes, and the top end of that range had nine rods and a sliding pin barrel, offering Westminster/Whittington/St Michael chimes. In the middle-price range came a clock with five coiled-tape gongs for Westminster chimes, the space within the clock case not allowing more. The monied end of the market, the customers for the large, ornate clocks similar to that by Rowley, would often have both bells and coiled-tape gongs fitted—bells for the lighter St Michael and Whittington chimes, gongs for the Westminster chimes and the hour strike.

Moving into the twentieth century, it is the German bracket-clock manufacturers who predominate. British makers were entrenched in other markets, and while it remained possible to obtain a British-made bracket clock, the German ones met a larger public, at around one-third of the price, for equivalent clocks. Some English makers took the 'If you can't beat 'em, join 'em' approach, offering their own cases with German movements. Catalogues from this period sometimes list clocks as English cases with 'W & H' or 'GB' movements—almost hoping, perhaps, that people would not realise that W & H meant Winterhalder and Hofmeyer, and the GB was not Great Britain but Gustav Becker, a prolific German manufacturer!

8

DECLINE, FALL AND REVIVAL

Throughout the latter years of the nineteenth century, two distinct revivals were running concurrently, the Gothic and the Empire; but the early years of the twentieth century leaned heavily towards the Empire, and brought a revival of lightness and delicacy. Perhaps after the solid but dour reign of Victoria, the new 'young' Edward, with his love of life and horses, recalled an age that was a hundred years past.

Furniture developed the inlay work, especially line inlay, of the Sheraton period, and in clock cases the full-arch top, balloon and Gothic styles were revived: the Gothic may seem out of place here, but the clocks of the twentieth century shed the ebonised cases and brass inlay that epitomised the menacing overtones of the true Gothic style. They came instead with a lighter case finish, often in oak with a light wood 'string' inlay. Some of these clocks may be mistaken for earlier styles, but there are basic differences. The most obvious one is the size: whereas the Gothic case of 1800 would stand upwards of 12 inches high, that of 1900 would rarely exceed 10 inches. The quality, too, should be apparent; by 1900 all parts of a medium-price clock would be mass-produced, the cases, especially, being manufactured in quantity to suit a particular range of furniture. As today (although the trend is now reversing somewhat), people wanted a clock that would not only fit into their home without dominating it but would also match their sideboard, display cabinet, etc. With a total population of nearly 40 million, the middle-of-the-range manufacturers could compete in a vast market. Most of these clocks were merely copies of an earlier style, adapted to suit current taste.

An example for more detailed study is shown in photograph 24. It is of English manufacture, but beyond that, the detail is vague—it could have been made by a firm such as Smiths, who were well established by this time. It stands 12in high and is 9in wide. The estimated date is 1900–1910. The case is in plain mahogany veneer and the mouldings are simple forms; the sole embellishments are the set of brass, cheese-shaped feet and the brass bezel. The case style is that of the full-arch top and may be compared with that of the Archard clock, (see photograph 12) although it must be remembered that these two clocks were made for different sectors of the market.

24 English-made, full-arch clock, c1900

25 Rear of full-arch clock

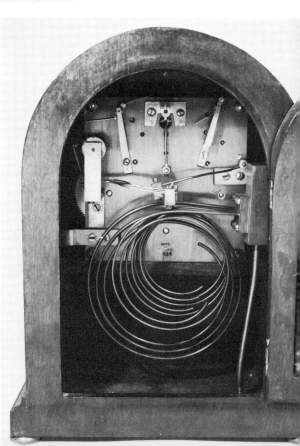

No longer is the dial painted: it has a silvered finish on a base-metal ground. This silvering method allowed the economy of using a thinner dial plate, and was also quicker. In clocks of this period, the outlines of the numerals and the chapter ring have often been pressed in to the dial on manufacture. Subsequently the numerals were finished by having hot wax melted into them, in the manner of the earlier brass dials, followed by a silvering process, the silver not adhering to the waxed portions. (Repair of this type of dial is also easier, since it does not involve repainting of the numerals.)

The movement of the clock is shown in photograph 25 and is very much a factory-produced unit. The words 'Made in England' appear on the backplate, together with a serial number, and this may have been done in response to a law passed in 1901 demanding that imported clocks must be stamped with the country of origin, or with some indication that they were of foreign manufacture. The movement is three-train, without a fusee in sight, all the trains being driven be spring barrels only. It was not that English makers could no longer manufacture fusees, since Smiths, as an example, were incorporating fusee drives into their skeleton clocks during this period; it demonstrates an attempt by the English volume-production companies to compete on equal terms with the Germans. There is a recoil escapement, with light lenticular pendulum-bob (not shown), and the workmanship, while not up to that of earlier clocks, is adequate, with solid pinions and robust plates. The chime is Westminster, as evidenced by the set of five coiled-tape gongs (four for the chime, with the largest one for the hour strike), the sequence being provided by the pin barrel on the left of the backplate. The whole movement is mounted, bracket-clock style, on a seatboard, supported by two L-shaped brackets.

From 1900 onwards, the movements of such clocks were fairly standard and, without some name on the backplate it is often almost impossible to determine whether they are of German or English manufacture. The same movements were also used in the smaller mantel clocks—which during the twentieth century became the most popular clocks of all.

German and English manufacturers were, at this time, competing in both the expensive bracket-clock market and the mantel-clock market; they would also be competing, alongside the Americans, for a share in the wall-clock market, the Germans with their version of the Vienna regulator, the Americans with their highly decorative dropdial clocks and the English with, in the main, the simple wall dial, with or without a fusee drive. Some German manufacturers, concerns such as Winterhalder and Hofmeyer, were supplying both markets; a few were concentrating on expensive products. One of these was Lenzkirch, whose wall regulators matched in quality those from some of the early Austrian makers; Lenzkirch also made bracket-clock movements and one of their clocks is illustrated in photograph 26.

Dating from 1900–1915, this clock typifies the revival of earlier, graceful styles in the more expensive end of the market. The case is in walnut veneer on an oak carcase and is of dome-top form, reminiscent of the late seventeenth-century styles, the plinth at the top of the dome being of curl-cut veneer—a sign of quality. A seventeenth-century clock would have had brass fretwork or castings to the door surround and the dome, but here some extremely well executed walnut carving is used; the German makers, especially in the Black Forest, where Lenzkirch had their factory, were expert in wood-carving (as evidenced from the better quality cuckoo-clocks from this area). The front door is full-width, fitted with a lock, and the rear door is of fretted wood, with a silk backing.

The dial is of brass, with a separate, silvered chapter ring in a style that had not been seen for many years; the dial centre is matted. The cupid's-head spandrels are a quality casting and in the style of the late seventeenth—early eighteenth century; the hands are fleur-de-lys pattern and are in keeping with the overall exuberance of the case. On the left-hand side of the dial is a rectangular cut-out; it serves no purpose in this particular clock, but this dial design was also used on clocks fitted with a strike/silent lever, necessitating a cut-out somewhere along the edge of the dial plate.

The movement (photograph 27) should be familiar by now, since it is almost identical to the one fitted to the Winterhalder and Hofmeyer clock, photograph 23, although Lenzkirch movements are generally of better quality. Again, it is a two-train movement, driven by spring barrels, the ting-tang quarter chiming being driven from the same train as the hour strike. A simple cam wheel provides the correct sequence for the chime, counted on the hour rack, and as in the Winterhalder and Hofmeyer movement, one hammer is lifted clear of its coiled-tape gong as the hour approaches, so that the hour strike, on a rack and snail, is sounded on the other hammer. The movement has recoil escapement and is fitted with the Brocot-type suspension adjustment (the adjustment arbor can be seen immediately above the numeral XII on the dial); the plates are plain and rectangular, containing well-finished wheels and solid pinion leaves. A slightly unusual feature is that the pillars are pinned to the plates—by 1900, screwed pillars were in fairly general use, but Lenzkirch tended to continue with a design similar to that used in their wall regulators.

26 Lenzkirch domed-top clock, c1910

27 Rear of Lenzkirch clock

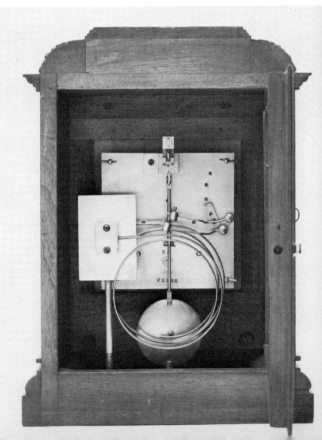

Lenzkirch manufactured quality clocks until, like many other German manufacturers, they succumbed to the recession in Germany in the late 1920s. They ceased to trade shortly after 1930; their original premises are now a cosmetics factory—from one face to another!

From 1910 to 1920, several fashions were in evidence, the main theme, probably, being mock Tudor or mock Jacobean. Furniture, and clocks, tended to grow in size and to assume heavy decoration, usually in the form of carving. A minor theme was the Empire–Sheraton, much modified, with line inlays and simple, legible dials.

The First World War of course disrupted trade in clocks, especially from Germany and to a lesser but significant extent from America. To illustrate the depth of penetration of the British market by German manufacturers, the early years of the war brought a shortage of that essential item the alarm clock: so much of this market had been supplied by the German and American makers. After the war, the Americans never again quite achieved their pre-1914 volume, but the Germans were quick to re-establish their British outlets. They could still make and sell, at a competitive price, a complete range of clocks, including bracket clocks.

Many authors tend to dismiss these clocks because they do not have the quality of the English bracket clock, which in their opinion was extinct after 1850. I can understand the feelings of authors such as Cescinsky and Webster, for when their classic book *English House Clocks* was published in 1913 they were experiencing at first hand the almost total domination of the market by German makers, and the apparent demise of the English art of clockmaking. However there are two factors to be considered:

1 The clocks of the period 1900–30, whatever their comparative quality, are clocks of their time and the antiques of the future. Some of them, in my opinion, are attractive—the Lenzkirch clock, photograph 26, is only one example, and is from the middle price range; above that were even better examples of both German and English manufacture, some with fusee drives.

2 The art of clockmaking did not die, but became diversified into other horological fields; and certainly it went into partial hibernation, awaiting the return of better times.

Photograph 28 shows a bracket clock from the medium-price range. It was made in about 1920, the only outward sign of its provenance being the legend 'Wurtemburg' printed at the lower edge of the dial; it stands 13in high and is 8in wide. The case, in mahogany veneer, is of the break-arch style, and combined with the full-arch dial it is reminiscent of a style that evolved during the first quarter of the nineteenth century. In place of

28 German chiming clock

the supporting columns to the arch, this clock has machined 'fluting';
the decoration consists of a single carrying handle to the top of the arch,
spun-brass cheese feet and a brass 'bezel'. As on many of the German
clocks of this period, the front door is mainly of glass, bevelled at the
edge and supported in a thin brass bezel, to which is screwed a solid
metal, silvered, dial mask.

The dial is of sheet metal, and originally had a silvered finish over the copper coating on the base metal. It is this copper coating that creates problems when repairing the dial, and I am informed that an attempt at re-silvering the much-worn dial failed after three attempts—the copper coating insisted on appearing through the silver finish. Finally, in desperation, the dial was painted instead. To my mind, this repair is not only acceptable (see later chapter on restoration and faking), but rescues what would otherwise remain an unsightly dial. The chapter ring is of 6in diameter. In order to contain the winding holes within the chapter ring, the winding arbors drive the spring barrels through an intermediate gear set, fitted to the front plate. The hands are of the spade form, the most used design from this period onwards, although the minute hand is slightly elaborated, the correct description being 'light double-swell spade'. In the dial arch are the two subsidiary dials, the left-hand one being the regulator for the pendulum up-and-down work (the dial markings being for decoration only) and the right-hand one being the chime/silent lever.

The movement is a factory-produced unit, of reasonable quality although it does have the 'lantern' pinions of cheaper design; it is three-train with spring barrel drive, recoil escapement and a pin barrel for the Westminster chime. The chimes are on four rod gongs, with the hour strike using the fifth gong, together with two of the chime gongs, to produce a chord; this method was introduced in the latter years of the nineteenth century as an economy measure—it was more expensive to fit one coiled-tape gong just for the hour strike (although some clocks have this, and are obviously from the expensive end of the market), but if the hour was struck on just one rod gong it sounded a little feeble, following on from the chime sequence; the few clocks that have this system are usually from the period 1890–95. The answer was to have the hour-strike mechanism fitted with an arm which lifted two or more of the chime hammers at the same time as the hour hammer was lifted. This chord provided an effective contrast to the single notes of the chime.

BRACKET CLOCK TO MANTEL CLOCK

Although mantel clocks of various designs were made throughout the nineteenth century, it is likely that the eponymous mantel clock of the period from 1920, the 'Napoleon-hat' clock, had its origins in the bracket clock. This clock, still manufactured today, came into prominence as a cheap, reliable timekeeper that would fit the mantelpiece of the average sitting-room; few, if any, of the bracket clocks we have discussed would fit this particular site, which with even well-off homes

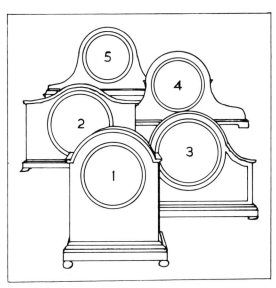

29 Five clocks showing the transition from bracket to mantel clock

becoming generally smaller and lower-ceilinged would become the focal point of the whole house. I have attempted to illustrate this transition from bracket clock to mantel clock in photograph 29, using as an example the break-arch case style. I am not suggesting that this was *the* transition, but it could have been a logical progression, not forgetting that the true bracket-clock form of case remained available to the wealthier client. (Photograph 29 should be read in conjunction with figure 43 which shows the clocks in outline form.)

The bracket clock (1), is an example from, I believe, the late nineteenth century. It was typical of bracket clocks at the cheaper end of the market and is a timepiece movement in a plain, mahogany-veneered case; the sole decoration is the moulded frieze at the bottom of the front apron, and the brass caddy-ball feet. The 6in diameter convex dial is painted and the brass bezel is secured by a key-lock. The movement is single fusee with a chain drive, contained between robust plates; the escapement is of the recoil type, as in all the clocks illustrated here. It is virtually impossible to determine the country of origin, apart from the fact that by its style and method of manufacture, it must be either English or German. The clock stands 13in high, and is 9in wide, 6½in deep, of sufficient size to fit the Victorian mantelpiece.

The next clock (2), in chronological order, dating from about 1910, must be termed a mantel clock, by my definition, since it is wider than it is tall, standing only 11in high and being 13in wide and 6½in deep. However, it is a break-arch case, although the arch is now flattening out. The case is in mahogany with an edge inlay of lighter wood, and there is a hint of quality to the cast-brass ogee feet (similar to the eighteenth-century patterns) and the solid feel of the bezel; the bezel, here, is locked but no longer with a key—it locks against a spring-loaded button in the left-hand side of the case. The convex dial is silvered on a brass-sheet ground and the hands, although mass-produced, are of an elegant form, similar to the 'unifoil' shape of the 1820s.

The picture suggests, from the position of the left-hand winding arbor, that it has a two-train movement, which indeed it has, but a chime/silent lever can be seen to the left of the numeral IX—an apparent contradiction. However, a glance at the movement reveals all! It is a chiming movement, sounding Westminster chimes on four coiled-tape gongs, with the hour struck on a fifth gong. The basic difference with this movement is that it sounds the chime only up to the three-quarter hour point—at the hour there is no full chime, but the hour strike only—what is known in the trade as a three-quarter chime. I have already mentioned that it is possible to obtain the ting-tang chime and hour strike using just one spring barrel, but that the total power available from the usual size of spring barrel would be barely sufficient to drive the train for a week. It is unlikely, then, that even a three-quarter chime could be supplied from one standard barrel; in this clock, as in most of this type, the chiming-barrel size is increased to take a longer spring. Two-train chiming movements also need some device to 'tell' the mechanism that the next operation is the hour and not the next chime sequence; on this clock, at the approach of the hour a cam pushes the chime barrel out of gear, while at the same time it pushes into gear a single pin to operate the hour hammer. Obviously a complicated system, of one type or another, must be used to separate the two functions of chime and hour strike, and, as we have seen, the chime provision entails the fitting of an oversize spring barrel. The total cost of such a system is still cheaper than a three-train movement.

I have gone to some length to explain this particular system, since it was used, although rarely, during the eighteenth and nineteenth centuries. The clock just described was made by Winterhalder and Hofmeyer and is a good-quality movement of nicely-finished plates and wheels, and solid pinion leaves.

Third in chronological order (3), is a clock by the Hamburg America Clock Company (HAC), 10½in high, 13in wide and 5in deep. This manufacturer is easily recognised by the trade mark of two arrows, crossed; the mark will usually be found on the dial (it is just visible in this photograph, below the numeral XII and above the hand arbor) and is usually repeated on the backplate. The break-arch style of case is still retained in this clock, dating from about 1915–20, as is the line inlay clearly seen on the front apron, in the Regency style; the case itself is in a very well-figured mahogany veneer. The dial and bezel are, by now, a mass-produced item, the dial being a thin, flat disc, silvered, with painted-on numerals, the bezel a much thinner section than on the previous clock, with a clip fastening to the case. The movement is mass-produced and is mounted, not on a seatboard, but by screws to the inside front of the case. This becomes the commonest fixing from about 1910 onwards, made possible partly by the fact that the average mantel-clock movement was not more than half the weight of the equivalent fusee movement of the nineteenth century. The strike is on the hour and half hour, on a coiled-tape gong.

The HAC company were founded in 1874, entering the market at the peak period of German and American competition for the English market; in the economic collapse of Germany after World War I, many companies went bankrupt, although HAC survived until 1930, when they merged into the Junghans group. Junghans had been their rivals in the cheaper clock market (shelf clocks and small timepieces), but their production methods enabled them to weather the economic storms of the 1920s. The company exist today, their main output being quartz movements for clocks, as it is for another rival surviving from the 1920s, Kienzle.

The fourth clock (4), has an interesting origin. Made during the period 1925–30 by the Garrard Clock Company, it stands 9in high, 13in wide and is 5½in deep. It has the vestige of a break-arch case, although this is but a single moulding running across the arch; the case is veneered in burr walnut, a particularly attractive pattern, and has moulded wooden feet. The dial is simple, with arabic numerals (which from this period on, became the more usual style) and is silvered on an alloy base. The movement, however, is of more interest—it is three-train, with spring barrels, sounding Westminster chimes on rod gongs. The unusual feature is that there is provision for three modes—'chime', 'hour strike only' and 'silent', this being a useful feature once the radio era had arrived—the clock could tell the listener when to switch on the radio set, but would then not disturb him by sounding off the chimes at each quarter. A lever lifts the chiming hammers clear of the pin barrel, so that although the pin barrel goes through its sequence, triggering off the hour strike at the end, the chime does not sound. The chiming does not lose its sequence, as could happen on earlier clocks, although by 1920 mantel clocks were featuring automatic reversal to the correct sequence, irrespective of when the lever was returned from 'silent' to 'chime'.

The back plate is finished with a machined whorl pattern, which while not having the quality of engraving does give a better finish than its competitors had at this period. An additional feature is a set of spring clips inside the case, to hold the pendulum and the key when the clock is in transit.

That the quality of this clock compares well with others of its age, is not surprising when one considers the manufacturers. The Garrard Company were founded in 1915 to manufacture munitions; after the war, they turned to that other entertainment medium—the spring-driven gramophone. It was a minor step to transform a clockwork motor into a clock. Nowadays, of course, they are a leading name in record-turntable design and manufacture, and a part of Smiths Industries.

Mention of Smiths Industries introduces the last clock in the illustration on page 143. This was made by the Enfield Clock Company, founded in 1929 by Carl Schatz. The company competed directly with German and American imports, producing a wide range of clock movements, from simple timepieces through wall clocks and striking movements, up to the double and triple chime movements. In 1933, however, the severe competition, especially from established companies such as Junghans and Kienzle, forced them nearly to bankruptcy; the major holding in the company was bought by Smiths Industries, who for many years retained the Enfield name on a range of clocks.

The clock shown is the plain, Napoleon-hat shape, dating from about 1930–35, standing only 9in high, but now wider, this one being 16in across and 5½in deep. The case is of oak veneer on a softwood carcase and is devoid of decoration except for moulding to the bottom of the apron. The dial is silvered, with printed numerals, the hands being the sole outstanding feature. These are a nice (mass-production) style of the serpentine form (see figure 21), which had its peak of popularity from 1760 to 1800, before being replaced by the more delicate patterns of the Regency period. Several clocks of the early twentieth century had this form of hand, since it complemented the revival of Jacobean-style furniture which continued into the 1930s. The movement is of rather better quality than one would expect from a German clock of this type (the Americans never produced this style of case), and perhaps this is the reason why Enfield eventually succumbed—mass-market customers were less concerned with the innards of the clock than with the price paid and the outward appearance. The chime is Westminster on rod gongs, mounted on the backplate, a feature already on the wane, in the interests of space; after 1930, the chime gongs were increasingly often put *beneath* the movement, slimming the clock's overall width.

The revival in Jacobean furniture also revived the longcase clock, far removed from the original style and usually with heavy carving or decoration to the case, often with glass panels to the front door and tubular-gong chiming movements. Bracket clocks, too, followed this trend, both English and German makers producing examples in large, heavily decorated cases during the period 1915–30. Fusees were retained on expensive examples and more clocks appeared complete with wall brackets. It has been suggested that the bracket clock during the 1920s went the way of the longcase in the 1850s, becoming larger and fussier in style in a bid to demonstrate its pedigree. A great number of these clocks was produced during this period, mostly within three ranges—the German movement in a German case, the German movement in an English case, and the English movement in an English case, the latter being about three times the price of the German clock.

POST-SECOND WORLD WAR CLOCKS

But with the Second World War, the demand for German products of course declined once more. The years from 1940 to 1960 are ill-documented as far as bracket-clock development is concerned; many records were lost in the war, and again Britain went through a postwar depression. Mantel clocks reappeared in quantity once supplies of timber were restored, with Smiths Industries taking a prominent place under their house names of Empire, Astral and Enfield. The German manufacturers never again established a stranglehold in that particular market and never re-entered the bracket-clock field. No English maker, as far as I know, produced bracket clocks in any quantity, although there are occasional examples by firms such as Dents, the chronometer makers; they offered a Tompion-style bracket clock during the early 1950s. (No doubt I shall be called to task for missing the fact that some Fred Bloggs produced 10,000 bracket clocks in 1955—I will add any such substantiated material to the second edition of this book!)

A turning-point came about 1960, however. Britain was entering a decade of plenty and clockmakers ended their hibernation. Among smaller clocks on offer today is one in Napoleon-hat style with—guess what—a German movement; the Kieninger Company of Germany produced good-quality movements suitable for a wide range of clocks. More important is the revival of British clockmaking skills. The clock-trade magazines are filled with advertisements from clockmakers, case makers, movement makers and restorers—at their worst producing reasonable-quality movements and at their best able to restore a missing or broken part to a standard defying detection.

For the wealthiest 20 per cent of the population who wish to buy new, and not antique, there are clocks available at a price comparable with that of the eighteenth-century bracket clock; these will not be unique examples (nor were most of the eighteenth-century ones), but *will* be examples of craftsmanship.

A particular clock in today's market is shown in photograph 30. It stands 16in high, and is made by Sinclair, Harding and Bazeley. It is not intended to be a reproduction of any particular period, but has brought together several styles that the makers feel combine to achieve an overall balance of design. The case is veneered in either mahogany or English walnut (the latter is now again being used for veneers of distinctive appearance), the case being of the break-arch design (1780), with good quality brass castings for the carrying handle and ogee feet. The glass panel is in the style of clocks up till the end of the eighteenth century.

The dial is of break-arch form (1720), and is of brass with a separate silvered chapter ring. The spandrel design dates from around 1710–20, and the dial centre is matted (or frosted), with the makers' cartouche in the position adopted by several early eighteenth-century makers, once the recoil escapement made obsolete the mock pendulum aperture. The hands are of the non-matching type, similar to those used during the period

30 Modern bracket clock by Sinclair, Harding & Bazeley

1720–60; the strike/silent lever is in the usual position for a break-arch dial.

The movement, not shown here, refutes any argument that craftsmanship has gone. It is a three-train, fusee-driven mechanism, with recoil escapement, chiming on either four (Westminster) or eight (Whittington) bells, with the additional feature of a chime/silent provision fitted to the upper left side of the back plate; the hour strike is on a single bell. The back plate is engraved in a style which though perhaps more mechanistic than that used in the seventeenth and eighteenth centuries, is very attractive.

I have illustrated just one of the many fine clocks available today from makers both ancient and modern—the omnipresent Thwaites and Reed (now merged into the Elliott Clock Company) have recently reintroduced styles of bracket clock that were popular in the days when they themselves were a jobbing company. Virtually all the traditional types of clock are obtainable, ranging from carriage clocks through 'Vienna regulators', bracket clocks, longcases and wall dial clocks to—for example—a fine reproduction of a seventeenth-century architectural-top hooded wall clock, in the Edward East style, by Richards of Burton. These clocks are competing for a share in the same slot in the market that attracted the seventeenth-century makers, the people who do not buy a clock merely to be told the time but want it to convey a certain status to their homes and to be admired as a piece of intrinsic beauty.

Thus we have come full circle in the development of the bracket clock in Britain. Wishing to avoid describing only the most prestigious clocks, I have dwelt in the main on clocks that are still attainable to the collector of modest means. I have also tried to show the bracket clock in a more 'archaeological' sense, set against its background of social, economic and technological life during specific periods. Collectors and dealers too often take a blinkered approach to clocks; some will not accept that, by the middle of the eighteenth century, bracket clocks were only rarely a unique piece of work; in part, if not wholly, they were the product of jobbing workshops. I can whisper the name of Tompion, in hushed reverence, in the best of circles, but I wonder what 'honest' George Graham, if he were alive today, might say—perhaps something like this: 'Yes, my friends, Master Tompion was a good clockmaker—better than that, he was the best Public Relations Officer our little company ever experienced. As to the quality of his clocks, consider if you will the quality of the craftsmen that did work for him. It is a fact of life, gentlemen, that a successful man can attract unto himself the flower of apprentice genius, who will perforce produce the best clocks ever to appear under the name of the man.'

The point to bear in mind is that each stage in the development of the bracket clock represented a facet in the life of someone, somewhere, sometime. Its development has spanned virtually the whole of British horological history. It has competed with passing fashions in longcase clocks, wall clocks, carriage and mantel clocks, and has outlived most of them. A particular clock may appear ugly to our eyes, but in its own time it may have represented the height of fashion and/or taste—set against its own background it will assume its true stature.

9

COLLECTING BRACKET CLOCKS

There is nothing like experience when it comes to assessing clocks; but with a little care expensive mistakes can be avoided—though remember that even practised dealers and collectors *can* be mistaken. In this chapter I hope to reduce the odds that, when you dash off to buy your first bracket clock, you pick a 'wrong 'un'. It helps, of course, if you already have some skill in the repair of clocks or in dealing with them—the more clocks that pass through your hands, the more a pattern begins to emerge in your mind of what a clock should look like. With experience, you can make a fair guess at what lies behind the dial even before opening the rear case door. But if you are not already steeped in clock lore, then ask the advice of the local repairer who specialises in bracket clocks. Better still, if he is short-handed, offer to do some of the more mundane and less skilled tasks that could save him a little time but not cost him too much if you made a mistake. By the time clock cleaning fluid has soaked into the knife-edge cuts made by wirewool, and callouses have developed to match the tenosynovitis brought on by 'pegging out' pivot holes, you will have learned something about clocks. Listen to the repairer—if he loves clocks, and some of them still do, he will not mind answering questions—for he can tell you what is repairable, at what cost, or what would be so expensive to repair that the end would not justify the means. Not only that, but if he has been repairing clocks for many years he will know the particular idiosyncracies of certain clocks, and how to deal with them.

GETTING TO GRIPS

If you are inexperienced in the workings of clocks, I suggest that the next stage is to take a clock apart and put it back together again, without any parts left over. I have heard it said that the best clock movement to practice on is one from an English bracket clock of the early to middle nineteenth century, the reason being that such movements are so sturdily constructed as to defy the worst machinations of the tyro! However, unless you can acquire an old movement that has perhaps lost its case, this may prove to be an expensive exercise. Nor would I recommend that you start on an old German or American movement from one of the lower-price clocks, since some of these are so flimsily constructed that they, or you, are easily damaged. A friend was once showing me one particular German movement of the type that has 'skeleton' plates, where there is metal only where it is needed for pivot holes, etc, the remainder being cut away for reasons of economy. With the movement in its complete state, and bolted together, he demonstrated that he could flex the plates by pulling them apart; unfortunately he flexed them to such a degree that the spring-barrel teeth lost contact with the teeth of the great wheel, and the mainspring unwound in an instant, the spring-barrel teeth taking a slice out of his thumb. Little wonder that an old clockmaker acquaintance calls these movements 'mousetrap clocks'. It is better to practice on an old mantel clock, preferably one with an English movement, or failing that one with a solid-looking German movement.

It is possible to dismantle a movement from a clock of the kinds described above with tools you would have around the home, but if you intend to oil (at least) your own clocks, it is better to obtain the following basic tools from one of the tool stockists appearing in the horological magazines:

> set of watchmakers screwdrivers
> 6in screwdriver
> pair of snipe-nose pliers
> pair of side cutters
> pair of end cutters
> 2oz clock hammer
> tweezers
> eyeglass or magnifying-glass

As far as the hardware is concerned, I would buy items of good quality, especially the small screwdrivers; if you have no difficulty in retaining an eyeglass, a 4× magnification is good enough to start with, otherwise it is difficult to keep the object in focus. I also suggest the addition of a small adjustable spanner (monkey-wrench in the USA): this would be viewed with some hilarity by most professional repairers, who rarely if ever use spanners of any kind, but I find it useful for the threaded pillar fixings on later clock plates, as well as on other small jobs. The only other requirements, before you start, are cleanliness and care; prepare a clean, tidy work-surface with a selection of trays or boxes to hold the components. It is beyond the remit of this book to delve into clock repairing, and there are other, excellent books on this subject, therefore I will deal only with the taking apart and putting together of the movement, points to note, and oiling of the movement after assembly.

Releasing the power

The first rule is, *always* release any spring power *before* attempting any work on the movement.

For a spring-barrel drive movement, the sequence is as follows. Take hold of the movement in one hand, in such a way that one finger is positioned on the tail of the ratchet (or click) on the spring-barrel arbor. With the other hand, fit the winding key to that arbor, and turn it as you would in winding the clock; then, whilst maintaining pressure on the key, release the ratchet from engagement with its wheel. At this point, you will be holding against the spring power. *Slowly* allow the key to unwind, maintaining your grip, and—unless you are a contortionist—you will be able to unwind the key through about half of one complete turn. Release the ratchet, ensuring that it engages with its wheel, take a fresh grip on the key and repeat the process until no more spring power remains; if the clock has a second train, repeat the sequence on that train.

The procedure for a fusee-driven movement is different. The ratchets on the fusee itself are usually inaccessible for this purpose, and the ratchet on the spring barrel cannot effectively be used for two reasons: it is difficult to obtain a purchase on the short arbor of the barrel, and there is more power to hold in a fusee spring barrel.

However, in a way a fusee drive is easier to handle. Hold the escapement wheel and remove the escapement pallets; take a hardwood dowel and apply this to the escapement arbor pinion as a brake. Let go the escapement wheel, controlling the speed of the train with the brake. (Do not try this method with a non-fusee system, since the lack of inertia will allow the train to rotate at high speed—a professional may be able to cope with this, but it is unwise for the beginner to take this short cut.) Once the power is off the fusee line, we still have to deal with the spring barrel itself, remembering that there is always residual power in the spring barrel from the initial setting up. The usual method here is to grip the short arbor in a mole wrench, or in the vice, and keeping a firm hold on the movement, release the ratchet by the method used previously for a spring barrel; there will be only six to eight ratchet teeth to release in the spring barrel.

To deal with the strike train, if fitted, the easiest method is to operate the striking sequence continuously, by holding off the locking piece, thus preventing the train from coming to rest at the end of its usual sequence. The train may be allowed to run, since the air-brake (or 'fly') will act as a speed governor; once the main power is off, the spring-barrel residual power may be released as before.

Dismantling the movement

Once the power is removed, the movement may be dismantled, but remember that once the pillar fixings are removed, the movement will, literally, fall apart. Study the positions of the components first and if in doubt, make a sketch; ultimately, a component *will* only fit in one place, but it makes life a little easier if you know where that place is.

Remove the pillar fixing pins (or screws on later clocks) and place the components in boxes or trays—it will help if you separate the strike train and the going train—being careful not to damage the more delicate components, such as the escapement wheel and the fly, since it will do them a power of no good to drop a spring barrel on to them. Especially on older clocks, be sure that you mark the spring barrels (and fusees, if fitted) in some way, since they may vary in dimensions and must be replaced in the train from which they originally came.

At this stage, check the components for wear or repair. Examine the wheel teeth under the eyeglass for 'rounding off' at the tips of the teeth, suggesting that the clock has had a 'run' at some time, and check that the wheel is running true on the arbor. Examine the pinions for wear, looking for rounding of the pinion leaves due to age or incorrect depthing, and especially on old clocks check for the 'hollowing' effect, where the wheel has been in contact with one part of the pinion for many years. Then examine the pivots, looking for roughened bearing surfaces resulting from age or lack of oil; the pivot holes come next and may by now have developed an oval shape, due to the pressure of the train applied in one direction. It is often surprising how long a clock will continue to run in an extremely worn state.

An experienced repairer can, of course, correct normal wear of this type by rubbing down the pivots until they once more present a smooth bearing surface, rebushing the worn pivot holes to suit the new pivots and repairing the pinions, either by moving the arbor fractionally, to bring a new pinion surface into contact, or by renewing the pinions. Such repairs are not within the scope of this book, but the beginner will begin to realise the amount of restoration that could be necessary on an old movement. The movement may also visually demonstrate the work of the bodger, and any knowledge gained in this area may serve well for the future; check the escapement wheel and pallets,·as this is the favourite spot for a bad repair. If there seems to be a deal of soft solder around, be suspicious—soft solder *is* used in clock repair, but only to a minute degree, and it will not normally be visible. I have seen clock movements in which I would swear that the total weight of the solder is more than that of the brass work, with solder round the pallets, the escapement wheel and the striking levers, and it has even been used to hold the wire cable or chain to the fusee spring barrel.

Return, briefly, to the pivot holes, another favourite area of shoddy workmanship; it is quite common to find that these holes have been 'punched up' to avoid a rebushing job. If the holes have been worn into an oval shape, it is possible to return them to a circular one by punching the brass surrounding the hole, forcing the metal across the oval; fortunately, this is easy to detect, especially as it is usually performed on the outside of the plate (to save time in dismantling the movement) and can be seen by looking at the movement whilst it is still in the case.

Some of the above points may not seem important, but it must be remembered that any tampering with an expensive clock not only decreases its value but also increases the cost of restoration. Also, do not think that the bodger is a present-day phenomenon—you will find examples of his work appearing as soon as the early clocks were due for repair. I am not referring to those who converted early crown-wheel escapements to the recoil type, since in their day this was not horological rape; they were fulfilling a demand for the better timekeeping allowed by the recoil escapement system. It is not uncommon, however, to find a complete chiming train missing, removed in order to keep the clock going without the cost and time of repairing.

Springs and barrels

In clock restoration, you get what you pay for—it is never wise to take an expensive clock to someone who merely dabbles. How far you go yourself in dismantling is a matter for your own skill and confidence, but if you want to take out the springs from the barrels remember that it can be quite a job to replace them without the facility of a winder (used to pre-coil the spring), especially on a fusee drive, with its much heavier spring. An old clockmaker once told me the story of the 'demented spring barrel'. Whilst he was an apprentice, he was attempting to replace a spring in a barrel, when he lost his grip on the barrel, which shot across the workbench, crashed through the shop window and went rolling away down the hill. The story may have developed over the years, but the basis is true—there is a deal of power in a fusee-drive spring.

The springs in non-fusee clocks are less of a problem, and can be replaced by hand; what the job needs is care and patience, otherwise you may end up with a buckled spring, or at least score-marks inside the spring barrel. After replacing the spring introduce a few drops of the correct oil between the leaves and replace the cover plate. The spring end should look like that shown in figure 2a; otherwise, as in the example shown in figure 2b, the spring could fail prematurely. To remove the spring, you will find a slot in the barrel cover; in theory, you should be able to lever off the cover by inserting a screwdriver into this slot, but in practice it can sometimes be difficult to achieve this without damage to the cover or the lip of the barrel. If this seems likely, then tap the arbor to dislodge the cover plate, using a wooden mallet (or the clock hammer with a hardwood block—never with a metal-to-metal contact) and draw out the spring, keeping it loosely coiled until you can lift it clear of the nib where one end clips into the barrel. The practice of tapping the arbor is often frowned upon since it can lead to distortion of the barrel cover and the possibility of a damaged arbor pivot. However, this method, applied carefully, is preferable to having to butcher a recalcitrant cover with a screwdriver.

Check for splits or kinks in the spring, and for scoring within the barrel; any burrs may be removed with emery paper, but spring repairs are best left to an expert, since the spring may need retempering after repair.

Whilst on the subject of springs, check the click springs (if it is a simple spring-barrel system) for resilience—on French clocks, particularly, these small, single-leaf springs can esily lose their temper. If they break in service, it can be disastrous, since the owner will not discover the fault until he comes to wind the clock. The time they break is only in the winding, where, instead of the click spring forcing the click into mesh as each tooth of the click wheel passes, the spring breaks and the click falls away. A tip here is to listen for the clicking sound while winding, especially as the winding commences—if the click does not sound, then at all costs do not let go of the key, otherwise the train will go through its eight-day cycle in a very short time! Keeping pressure on the key, turn it in reverse, using both hands to retain a hold if possible, until the spring power is released. On to less exciting things.

The details of strike mechanisms have been discussed in earlier chapters and if the mechanism was operating satisfactorily when the movement was dismantled, there is nothing to note here; if repairs are necessary, beyond an obvious fault, then experience is called for and the beginner should entrust this work to a professional.

Pendulum suspension

The final component for examination is the pendulum suspension, since this device is probably the most ill-treated component in the entire mechanism (see section on care of clocks). The heart of the suspension is a thin strip of spring steel, fixed at the upper end and carrying the pendulum rod at the lower end; the thinner this strip is, consistent with having enough strength to carry the pendulum, the better it is, and you may chance upon a clock with a suspension strip of silk, in place of steel, found more often in French clocks. The principle of the strip is to provide as little resistance as possible to the action of the pendulum—to approach the ideal of a completely 'free' pendulum. It is important, therefore, that this strip is free from kinks and is of the correct dimensions to suit the weight of the pendulum. The pendulum itself should fit snugly into the crutch, with just enough play to allow it to move with some degree of independence; too much play, and the effect will be to create a 'ghost' tick, as the pendulum rod contacts the crutch at each extremity of the swing.

On the suspension of English fusee clocks, the usual arrangement is a suspension strip rivetted to the pendulum-rod, with a crossbow at the upper end; the crossbow sits into a groove in a cantilevered bridge fitted to the top of the backplate. The crutch is usually not crutch-shaped but is a single stub; the pendulum rod, in this case, will have a longitudinal slot, into which the stub will slide.

French clocks usually have the true crutch-shaped crutch, the whole of the pendulum rod fitting into its arms. These French clocks, as well as some English and German clocks, may have a Brocot-type suspension fitted (this was discussed in detail on page 108). Note here how the fine adjustment is achieved with the suspension strip carried on a threaded rod, the rod being rotated by the arbor protruding through the dial front, operating via a right-angled set of gears. This component usually shows some wear, especially if the adjustment has reached one end of its permitted travel—the teeth of the right-angle gear set can be easily stripped by injudicious use of the adjustment key. On such clocks, there is usually a means of coarse adjustment on the pendulum-bob, and when first setting up the clock, it is wise to position the fine adjustment at the *centre* of its total length of travel; the course adjustment can then be used to obtain approximate accuracy, and after the clock has been left to 'soak' at its site temperature for several days, the fine adjustment can be made.

Cleaning and reassembling

If the clock movement is of any value, repairs should now be done. After this, or if the movement is merely a 'practice' one, reassembly may begin. Unfortunately it is far easier to dismantle a movement than to put it together again. If the movement is part of your collection, it should be cleaned before reassembly, but since this usually involves immersion in a cleaning fluid, the spring barrels (and fusees, if fitted) will have to be dismantled completely. All clock-cleaning fluids are corrosive to some degree, and the few so-called repairers who merely 'dunk' the movement, complete, in a cleaning bath, as a short-term economy, are heading for long-term disaster. All the surplus cleaning fluid *must* be removed, following the instructions applicable to the type of fluid.

Once you have cleaned the movement parts, handle the components with care as you reassemble them, holding the plates by the edges only, and using tweezers when fitting the wheels, etc; otherwise the chemicals in the sweat glands of your hands will result in 'burn' marks on the brass components. These can be difficult to remove, especially since they will usually appear only after the movement has been assembled.

Take the back plate and lay it on a flat, steady surface, preferably across a tray, with only the plate edges in contact. This is done so that the components that will protrude through the back plate, such as the barrel arbors, are allowed to seat properly. On the back plate put the spring barrels (and fusees, if fitted, making sure that the lines are seated correctly and are free to run). Ensure that the spring barrels are replaced in their original positions. The trains can then be placed in position, omitting the pallets for the moment. You will now have a small forest of arbors, ready to receive the front plate.

If the movement is a fusee drive, the line should be connected to the spring barrel and the fusee, using the correct terminal connection (depending on whether it is a gut, a chain or a wire line), and the barrel and fusee should then be fitted to the back plate. Allow the line to hang loosely but make sure that once the movement is assembled the line will be able to run on to the spring barrel and fusee without having to make a detour round a pillar or an arbor.

Fitting the front plate is not done by sleight of hand, even by an experienced repairer. It is a matter of patience, starting with the plate resting on one spring-barrel arbor; from this point the action is similar to closing a clam shell, fitting each pivot into its hole, working outwards from the spring barrel, until all the pivots are seated and the front plate drops with a satisfying click on to its pillars. At no stage must you force any action—if the pivots are seating correctly, the front plate will seat under gravity, and if it does not, check whether one pivot has been tilted out of true. An experienced craftsmen will make this job look easy, holding the back plate at eyelevel and fitting the pivots with a deft action of the tweezers. At least once you have tried it you will better appreciate how much knowledge and skill goes into clock repairing!

If the movement is a fusee drive, the line can now be run on. The important point here is that with all spring power off, the line should be wound round the *barrel*. To do this, slacken off the spring-barrel ratchet (so that the click is inoperative). Then, holding the line taut with one hand, rotate the winding arbor of the spring barrel clockwise until the line is wound on. Once the line is tight, the mainspring can be set up. Tighten the click screw and rotate the barrel (using pliers or a small wrench) through half to three-quarters of one revolution. You are now ready to check that the fusee is functioning correctly. Wedge the escapement wheel with a piece of softwood, then wind up the fusee, noting that the line runs evenly. At the end of winding, check that the stop-work (described in Chapter 2) operates. If all is well, remove the wedge from the escapement wheel and observe the action of the train as it runs down. For a double fusee movement, this procedure is now repeated on the strike train.

While replacing the strike train, ensure that the correct 'warning' is incorporated; this feature is described in Chapter 2, but briefly once the lifting-piece has been raised by the pin on the motion work, the wheel that is fitted with the warning stop-pin should turn through approximately half a revolution before it is arrested by the projection on the lifting-piece. At this point, the hammer should not yet have started to lift. If it has, the pin wheel which lifts the hammer tail must be taken out of mesh with the train and rotated in reverse, until the oncoming pin is just out of contact with the hammer tail. (On French roulant movements, this adjustment is simplified, since the pin-wheel arbor has its back pivot on a separate plate and can be fitted after the movement is assembled.) No damage will arise if this sequence is incorrect, but what may happen is that, on release of the lifting-piece, with the hammer partially lifted, the strike train has to overcome this extra load and will only reach operating speed after the first blow has been struck, so that the hammer blows do not sound in a regular rhythm.

Once the movement is assembled, check that it turns freely, then fit the striking levers and the motion work to the front plate; refit the pallets and, if all seems in order, wind up both trains. The movement is now ready for oiling, and since this job can be undertaken by anyone with a modicum of skill and knowledge, and does not entail dismantling of the movement, I will deal with it in a little more detail.

Oiling

As an introduction, do not think of using an oil other than that produced specifically for clocks; it may cost a little more than cycle oil or sewing-machine oil, but years of development have gone into producing the correct composition. The amount used at one oiling session is infinitesimal, thereby justifying the use of the best available at whatever the cost. As long ago as the mid-nineteenth century, Benjamin Vulliamy produced a treatise on the use of oils available at the time, the problems associated with them, and the suggested avenues of further research. The mineral oils in common use today were not available to those early clockmakers, who had to be content with vegetable oils or animal oil.

Vegetable oils are fine for frying your fish and chips or lubricating your high-performance two-stroke engine, but they are definitely not at home inside your clock case. They function well at constant high temperature, but their viscosity increases rapidly as the temperature falls, and even slight variations in temperature (such as occur in the modern, centrally-heated home) can convert them into something that resembles muddy wax. Animal oils gave good results, since they tend to have a high surface tension, giving them more cling, but their use, in these days of increased awareness of ecological balance, is diminishing.

Todays standard mineral oils, which rule our industrial and domestic lives, are again unsuitable for clocks, even in their most refined state; many of them contain additives which can cause electrolytic action where brass and steel are in contact, and since I have yet to see a clock that does *not* contain this combination (my purse does not stretch to a sixteenth-century 'iron' clock), I would not recommend them. So the only solution is to use the correct oil, available from a clock repairer or from one of the many dealers in horological equipment. Having got it, use it sparingly; one of the worst crimes for the beginner is over-oiling. When studying a clock movement, with all its rotating and sliding components, it may seem that the whole works would benefit from being immersed in a bath of oil—*wrong*. A clock, for the most part, relies on *dry* contact. For instance, a brass wheel in contact with a steel pinion is made to a sound engineering design requiring no lubrication: with a good tooth form, there is rolling contact and not sliding contact. The points that do need lubrication are those where sliding contact occurs—at the pivots, the sliding components of the strike train (where steel slides on steel) and the pallets at their point of contact with the escapement wheel. (The one exception to the latter is the jewelled pallets of some visible escapements.) One maxim applies here: if it does not seem to have enough oil, then it probably has enough oil.

To perform a complete oiling routine, the strike levers should be removed, along with the motion work, since on most clocks some of the front-plate pivot holes are behind these components. (The repairer, reassembling a movement will finish doing so first, to check that all is in order, before removing the above components again for oiling.)

Transferring the oil from the receptacle to the movement must be a controlled operation and is best done with a thin wire strand, one end flattened slightly to pick up the oil, the other end having a grip of cork or wood. An oiler can be made by extracting one strand of a multi-strand wire cable, but do not use galvanised wire—flakes of galvanising make an efficient grinding compound. Using a device such as this, minute drops of oil can be placed in the 'oil sinks' of the pivot holes, remembering not to fill the sinks, or you will end up with a line of oil streaks emanating from the pivot holes, once the clock is running. Again, it seems that these sinks are there to be filled with oil, whereas in fact acting as an oil sink is a secondary purpose; they are drilled as they are to reduce the bearing-surface area of the pivot. A drop of oil is permissible on any steel-to-steel contacts on the striking train and the most minute drop of oil is permissible on the pallet faces. Otherwise reassembly may be completed.

To close this section—please ignore any 'good old remedies' for oiling clocks. Most, if not all, of them are not founded on scientific facts, especially those concerning the use of paraffin. Many longcase clocks have suffered, in the past, from the old dodge of placing a glass of paraffin inside the bottom of the trunk, in the belief that the light vapour, on rising, will create a lubricating mist for the clock movement. Paraffin is for removing oil, not replacing it. Fortunately, bracket clocks are not large enough for this practice, but they have suffered from the use of other 'medicinal compounds'.

If the foregoing only serves to convince you that taking a clock movement apart is not for you, so well and good—you can still enjoy clocks, whilst appreciating a little more the work that goes into making them and repairing them. You may also appreciate that the repair of clocks of any value should be in the hands of those who will treat them with both empathy and sympathy.

BUYING A BRACKET CLOCK

This book can demonstrate, in a general sense, what should be apparent when studying any particular clock, and the dating charts in the final chapter should simplify this process; but the book cannot be a substitute for experience. We can, however, narrow the learning process by providing ourselves with a basic check list.

1   *Which type of clock do I want?*
If, of course, money is no object then this question is irrelevant as you may indulge your every whim. But few collectors are in this fortunate position. One thing is certain—'clock fever' is no different, once the bug bites, from any other form of collecting. There are many clock widows who will testify to this, although the clock widow can become a fanatic herself. I heard of one lady who changed her whole furnishing scheme because it did not match her husband's clock collection—and did so willingly. It is too easy, however, as most collectors will aver, to rush out and buy the first bracket clock that takes your fancy, and to add to this until you end up with clocks of a conglomeration of styles and

periods and no overall theme. You now have, say, three or four German bracket clocks of the late nineteenth/early twentieth century (since they are still available at a reasonable price), and one Regency and/or one Victorian English bracket clock. Moreover, you may have paid a high price for these clocks because they were the ones that you wanted and, whilst there is no doubt that any bracket clock is an investment, the time-span for any profit-taking is years rather than months. Along comes a particularly nice mid-nineteenth century clock, just as you have spent your budget (and perhaps a little more besides), and you are faced with the need to sell off, quickly, two of your German clocks to raise the money for your latest desire. This process can be repeated ad infinitum, so pause for a while before you start buying, and consider whether your collection should have a 'theme'. You could, say, collect bracket clocks from the entire period of development, choosing one from each fifty-year or twenty-five year period. This would be a really worthwhile collection, although there are two problems. One is money—a seventeenth-century bracket clock in good condition may cost you well over £2,000 (in 1982), and the prices are still rising. The second problem is more human and demonstrates what should have been one of the laws of Parkinson—as soon as you have paid out a substantial sum for a clock that, you are certain, is 'definitive' of the period, along will come a better one.

Another theme could be that of a particular period, one in keeping with both your taste and your pocket. You could choose, for example, the elegance of the Regency period, the simplicity of the early Victorian period, or the contrasting styles of clocks from 1870 to 1920. Most clock collectors, like collectors in other fields, go through several phases before they settle on one particular theme; it is similar to buying a house—the next one will be the perfect one for you, but after a short time you are planning extensions and alterations to make it a little *more* perfect.

2   *Where do I buy my bracket clock?*

In this area, you have three choices—a private sale, a dealer, or the auction room. Each has its advantages and disadvantages. For a private sale, the obvious sources are local and national newspaper advertisements or the 'for sale' section of one of the specialist magazines. The seller will be either another collector or a 'non-clock' person, selling off an inheritance. Most collectors are genuine, honest individuals but (dare I say it) they could have been misled and may be passing on a genuine mistake or an embarrassment. Find out, if you can, why they are selling and, from what you know, whether the price is reasonable—if it is much lower than you would expect to pay, be a little suspicious, since most collectors, though they often feign otherwise, know the value of their clocks. To set the record straight, however, I must repeat that the majority of collectors, in my experience, are only too happy to talk about their clocks and are genuinely interested in the clocks themselves, rather than a quick profit.

Should you come across an advertisement in the local press from, perhaps a little old lady, selling up to move into a smaller house, then this is a different approach, and *if* you have beaten the stampede of dealers, you may be in for a bargain; please, if the clock is grossly undervalued, offer a reasonable price, allowing for any necessary repairs. You have to live with your conscience. Even today there are still people who are duped by unscrupulous dealers who, for instance, will offer a high price for a mediocre bookcase if the owner 'will throw in the old clock—it might be useful for the timber'. I have known a clock to be bought this way, passed on through two or three dealers in as many weeks, then turn up at an expensive antique fair, two hundred miles way, with a price tag of ten times its original purchase price. Not only is this practice immoral, but these people have no love for clocks except as pieces of merchandise; over the last few years, they have denuded Britain of many fine clocks, sending container-loads to a Europe hungry to restore its war-ravaged antiques stocks. English bracket clocks and longcases are going the same way as French, German or Dutch clocks.

To offer a fair price may result in its own problems, of course. A dealer friend once offered a seller almost twice the asking price, and his offer was turned down on the basis that, if he was offering such an inflated price, then the clock must be worth far more! Sometimes one cannot win. Finally, beware of the advertisement that states 'no dealers', for although there are sellers who do not want the pressure of a dealer, most of these offers are made *by* dealers, as a message to other dealers to stay clear.

This brings me on to the second source of supply—the dealer. Not all dealers are grasping, money-hungry individuals; there are many who not only love clocks, but will be fair in their dealings, both buying and selling. If you decide to buy from a dealer, find one who specialises in clocks and one who will take time to explain their details; also, look for one who will guarantee the clock for a reasonable period of time. For this, you may have to find a dealer who is also a restorer. If the clock is in say, auction-room condition, the price should allow for an overhaul, remembering that, at 1982 prices, a two-train fusee bracket clock may cost upwards of £80 for an overhaul, before any necessary repairs are added. A dealer who displays the price of his clocks is preferable; some use coded letters, the excuse being that it depends who is buying. It is true that the trade buys from the trade, and at different prices than the public pay, especially since a dealer buying from another dealer would not normally expect a guarantee; but that is no excuse for not showing the asking price, in the hope that someone may come along who will pay far more than the clock is worth. It is impossible for me to indicate what price to pay for any particular clock, but from a study of prices you should be able to ascertain what is the average; variations from this should reflect the condition of the clock, and whether it has desirable or unusual features such as quarter chiming, or an engraved back plate, or bears the signature of a known maker. A clock is worth what you are willing to pay for it; you may be told by the pundits that you have paid more than the going price, but if you want the clock and are not needing a quick return on your capital outlay, then it does not matter, since the excess will be absorbed as the clock increases in value.

The third source of clocks is the auction room, and there are bargains to be had here, but there are also many more problems. First, because of the variety of items sold, few auction rooms have specialist knowledge; the city auction rooms may have a resident expert in clocks and the provincial auctioneers may have a local collector to run an eye over any clocks brought in, but these are in the minority. So most auction rooms play safe to cover themselves under contract law, especially on 'misrepresentation'. They may describe a bracket clock as 'Victorian', or 'Empire-style,' or simply 'antique' since the term 'antique' is now commonly accepted to include any item over fifty years old. The point to bear in mind, as the catalogue will state, is that the auction lots are sold as seen, and the *facts* of any lot must be verified by the *buyer*—the maxim *caveat emptor*, let the buyer beware, applies strictly.

The book should help in dating a clock and in checking for obvious doubtful points. A local repairer may offer to look over the clock for you, if you will pay for his time; but check that he has no connection with other interested parties. Allow yourself plenty of time—all auctions offer a viewing session—and armed with the catalogue, study the clock at your leisure. After allowing for any extra costs needed to bring the clock up to the standard you are seeking, decide on a price, but before finalising this check the catalogue for any 'hidden' costs: there may be VAT added to the bid price, if the clock has been put into the auction by a registered dealer (and I am always suspicious of such clocks). Also, the auction room charges a commission, and although the usual commission is paid by the seller and does not affect you, as the purchaser, some city auction rooms are charging a 'buyer's premium'. Such additions can increase significantly the apparent hammer price of the clock. (At the time of writing, the validity of this is being challenged.)

Many people, understandably, have a fear of auction rooms, resulting either from stories of a sneeze being taken as the last bid on something you do not want, or from thoughts of actually having to make a bid. As far as the first problem is concerned, this is largely a matter of ignorance, and watching too many comedy shows. Auctioneers are usually experienced men—they know when a bid is being made; if you do something which attracts their attention, they will ask, to your public shame, whether you are bidding; this will merely teach you to save any action such as fanning yourself with the catalogue, or waving to a friend, until the breaks between lots. As to the second problem, the fear of bidding, this is a natural trait, especially of the British. In an auction, there will be many other people, even dealers, whose hearts start to pound as a particular lot approaches. It happens to us all, in one form or another, but the regular auction-goers learn to disguise or control the feeling of rising panic.

One thing you must not do is to develop 'auction fever': many times I have seen a clock at auction knocked down for a higher price than it would have realised in a dealer's shop because someone could not stop bidding. Make a note of the price you want to pay and try to stick to that; at least, at an auction, you have the opportunity to outbid the dealers, since they will stop bidding at the trade price of the clock. If you come away from the auction feeling deflated because 'your' clock has been knocked down to someone else at only one bid higher than you were prepared to go, remember that person might have gone higher again had you carried on bidding.

A good reason for fixing an approximate maximum-bid price is that the bids might be 'run up', usually by a representative of the owner. A particularly desirable clock may come up for auction at a time when for one reason or another, the buyers who would pay a good price for it are not present. A 'reserve' price is put on the clock, below which it will not be sold; you may be able to find out what this reserve price is although many auction rooms will not divulge it. Let us say, for example, that there is a mid-nineteenth century bracket clock in the sale, with a reserve price of £500, though the reserve has not been stated; you have decided that you will bid a maximum of £450. Should yours be the highest bid, the clock would be withdrawn (usually by the auctioneer stating 'not sold'); however, if the owner's representative bid £475, this might cause you to decide that a further £50 is justifiable. You bid £500: the clock is sold, the owner gets his price, the auctioneer gets his commission and you get a clock which is more expensive than you had anticipated, but at least it is now yours. Incidentally, if a clock does not reach the reserve price, most auction rooms will allow you to submit a private bid after the sale is over, if you have decided in the cold light of day that the clock was worth a little more.

In the long run, however, it is best to stick close to your original price; you may lose one clock this way, but another will turn up eventually. Auction-room buying demands patience, tenacity and a single-mindedness that will not allow you to snap up a lesser clock simply because you are tired of waiting; if you are outbid for month after month, it might pay to assess whether you are undervaluing a particular type of clock.

Should you wish to forego the trauma of bidding, it is possible to leave a bid with the auction room, but check first exactly how the auction room operates this system; the most equitable way is one where you can leave a bid with one of the porters (and it pays to cultivate this invaluable breed). The auctioneer will not know what your maximum bid is, and the porter will bid as a private person (except where he has been commissioned to bid for two or more people for the same lot, in which case he will start bidding at the highest figure on his list), thus securing your clock at the lowest price. Beware the auction room where your bid goes to the auctioneer, since he will start at the highest bid he has on his list; this means that any further bid will put you out of the running. Apart from this, your high 'maiden' bid might frighten off the opposition and you will pay a price that might have been lower in an 'open market' system.

Auction rooms are fascinating places and you will learn not only the trends in clock prices, but a great deal about how people behave; the experience will be useful even if you have no intention of buying.

3   *Is the clock correct for its period and how much will it cost to restore?*
Here, the dating charts (pages 181–7) should be useful, remembering however that for every rule there is an exception. You should not expect to find, for instance, a German bracket clock with moonpoise hands, or an English bracket clock with fleur-de-lys hands, but one day you *might* find such a clock from a maker attempting to follow a particular fashion trend.

Escapement: one of the commoner conversions done on bracket clocks is from crown-wheel escapement to anchor escapement. It is fairly easy to determine whether this has been carried out. There will be 'spare' holes where the crown-wheel arbor mounting bracket was fitted and, probably, where the pallet arbor was taken out. Also, if you study the movement, there should be the obvious substitution of a new escapement and third wheel, together with the anchor-pallet arbor, since it would be impossible to fit these to the holes left from the crown-wheel escapement. The back cock, covering the pallet arbor, will have been removed and substituted by the bridge to hold the suspension strip of the anchor escapement. The style and quality of the work done should be obvious if it is, for instance, a Victorian conversion, where the repairer had no intention of faking but was merely fitting the more popular escapement of the time.

If you are considering the purchase of such a clock decide whether you will want it converted back to crown-wheel escapement, and how much the cost will be; remaking a complete crown-wheel escapement to an original standard, complete with back cock and bob pendulum, will not be cheap. However, if the conversion is an old one, it is not necessary to change it; it can be looked upon as a logical development in the life of the bracket clock, and a representation of a particular period in horological thinking.

Pull-repeat system: check for signs that a pull-repeat system was fitted originally, but is now missing; if you cannot study the movement itself, look for holes in the case and/or movement seatboard through which the pull cord would pass. A simple hour-repeat mechanism is a fairly straightforward job, but to restore a quarter-chiming mechanism, especially chiming on bells, is a skilled and costly undertaking. Removing a faulty quarter-chiming mechanism was a favourite bodger's trick to effect a quick repair, the owner usually accepting the story that the mechanism was 'beyond repair'.

Movement: checking the movement itself for wear on the wheels and pinions is obviously difficult before buying it—few sellers, including auction rooms, will allow you to take the movement out of the case. I poke a dentists mirror, lit by a pen torch, into the case, but if this is not feasible, look at the general condition of the back plate; if it is streaked with oil runs, and what you can see of the movement is not a pretty sight, assume that the movement will need at least a complete overhaul, and possibly some repair.

One item you can check is the operation of the springs and the two trains—especially with a private sale, since the clock should be working. In the auction room, the movement may be broken or have been allowed to run down. When visiting any clock for sale, I carry a set of 'star' clock keys, to cover every eventuality, and it is then easy to check for a broken spring and/or damaged strike train. A name on the dial or back plate is obviously a useful guide to dating a clock, but do not be too disappointed if the name does not appear in the reference books—not *all* makers are listed. If the signature is 'Fred Bloggs, Middlewich', a search of the Middlewich street directories (if you happen to be within travelling distance of the Middlewich Public Library) may reveal a retailer with this name. After 1775, most of the names on clocks will be retailers and not makers. Remember that the name could have been added at a later date.

Dial and hands: assuming for the moment that the clock is genuine, continue with an examination of the dial, checking for missing spandrels, the condition of the chapter ring on a brass dial, or the condition of the paintwork on a painted dial. It is possible to obtain a replacement spandrel by casting to the pattern of one of the remaining ones—at a price; if all the spandrels are missing, a replacement new set may be purchased from specialist dealers, although these will rarely have the look or feel of the originals.

The hands are probably more important than the remainder of the dial, since they are the components that are noticed first and that suffer most from the over-zealous owner. If they are broken or missing, it is possible to buy replacements for most styles from the specialist dealers, although again they rarely match the hand-finishing of the originals; on clocks made after about 1800, this matching is not such a problem, since by then the majority of hand sets were produced in quantity batches. In this case, you should ensure that the replacement hands are of the correct dimensions to fit the dial; the centre collets may need to be modified and it is important, visually, that the hands are of the correct length. The minute hand should terminate before, or on, the *outer* circle of the minute markings and should not be shorter than the *inner* circle of the markings; the hour hand may extend a little into the *inner* circle of the hour markings but it should not fall short of this circle. The dimensions, therefore, are critical and it is not just a matter of buying longer hands than necessary and cutting them down to fit, since any 'design' on the hands, such as the moonpoise, is intended to be seen at a specific distance between the root and tip—shortening the tip destroys the visual balance.

If your clock is an early one, it would justify the cost of an individual set of hands, made by one of the specialists in this field; such suppliers maintain stocks of patterns to suit any clock and will be able to advise you on the correct replacement.

If the painting on a dial is original, it will perhaps be in poor condition by now. From combination of metal polish, used to clean the dial, a constant scraping of fingernails across the dial when setting the hands, and criminal assault, using the winding key, it will have received its fair share of punishment over the years. Some purists maintain that one should retain the dial in its original state, otherwise one is destroying an intrinsic feature of the clock; this seems reasonable for very early clocks by famous makers, but generally it seems nonsense to have on view a beautiful clock marred by an ugly dial. Provided that you can find a good dial restorer and can order the repainting in the style of the period, using the dial itself (or photographs of similar clocks, in the case of a severely damaged dial) as a pattern, then I cannot see why the restoration should not be undertaken. In any case, should you come across a dial that is in pristine condition, then either the clock was stored away early in its life, or it has been restored at least once during its lifetime.

Clocks with stove-enamelled dials present more of a problem. It is difficult to repair cracked or chipped dials of this type, since the ageing process will have shaded the dial from its original bright finish, necessitating colour mixing of the filler paste and final coat to obtain a match; often a complete re-enamelling is necessary.

This is a suitable time to discuss any name on the dial. There may be a legible name which can be copied before the dial is rubbed down for repainting, and then transcribed on to the finished work. If the name is there, but is so worn as to be indecipherable (and there is no name on the back plate), study the dial under a strong source of light, turning it through various angles—ultra-violet light is excellent for this purpose—to see whether the odd letter is discernible. It is often possible to build up a name this way, even if only the place name and a few letters of the maker's (or seller's) name are available; a study of the reference books and/or street directories might then yield the complete answer. Should the name be completely illegible, study the movement closely, since there may be a name or company logo on the front plate, under the mounting brackets, on the bell stand or on the spring barrels. The Archard clock (Photograph 12) is an example of this research; the dial has been restored using the name Archard, a name which does not appear in the reference books of the time, and one which was possibly the name of the clock's owner. It would have been logical, had the name been completely illegible, to have added the name of Thwaites and Reed, the makers of the clock, who in any case sold clocks with their house name on the dial.

The detective work on an obscured name will often draw a complete blank. Yet many dials of the type, particularly the larger Regency dials, seem to cry out for a name to balance what would otherwise be a large expanse of plain dial; I believe that the *majority* of painted-dial bracket clocks had a name on the dial when new. So it would then be permissible to choose a name to suit the period of the clock. I am not suggesting a deliberate attempt to deceive, by adding a name such as McCabe or Ellicott, but the selection of an obscure retailer from a directory of the period of the clock and, preferably, one from outside the London area should the place name be similarly illegible. (There are buyers who will pay a premium for a clock that has the name 'London' on the dial, but, unless the clock is by a maker of renown, this reverence is completely misplaced; a clock made by a London workshop, sold by a London retailer, is no different from the same clock sold by a Norwich retailer.) It was common in the latter half of the nineteenth century for a large retail company who sold clocks as well as furniture, etc, to have the company name put on both the in-store clocks and the clocks for sale, Jas Shoolbred and Company and Payne and Company being just two examples. An amusing example of a private owner, a gentleman named Weslake, of King Street, Southwark, requesting his name on the dial is contained in the records of Thwaites and Reed for 1866. (This example was first uncovered by Ronald E. Rose during the research for his excellent book *English Dial Clocks*.)

> Dear Sir,
> I should like the name 'WESLAKE, LONDON' on the dial, but not too large. I suppose they are called block letters.
> I remain yours truly,   Weslake.

Mr Weslake was not sure of his grammar, but if he was buying a clock he was going to have his name on the dial.

So, if you want to write 'Fred Bloggs, Middlewich,' to replace an illegible name on the dial, do so with a clear conscience and without an intention to deceive. In my home town, there seems to be an inordinate number of antique clocks bearing the name of a well-known retailer of the nineteenth century (still in business today), but no harm results from this except, perhaps, to a few inexperienced buyers who think there is some special aura attached to a clock purporting to originate from their home town. To these I would say that, if they specifically want a local clock, the records of a local maker must be checked for sales and serial numbers, and the movement must be examined carefully for signs of an 'imported' product.

One final point on dial restoration is that some dials require careful consideration, especially the silvered dials on the German bracket clocks of the late nineteenth and early twentieth century. The dial plates of these clocks, for reasons of economy, were often made from thin sheet steel or alloy and, in order to obtain a suitable surface for silvering, were coated in a thin layer of copper. Once this layer wears through it is difficult, if not impossible, to obtain an even re-silvering; even when the layer is intact, the copper hue may appear as a blemish behind the silvering. As a last resort these dials are often rubbed down completely and restored with a painted finish instead of a silvered one, an acceptable procedure since many of these clocks were offered when new in a choice of silvered or painted finish. The Wurtenburg clock (photograph 28) is a case in point—I am told that resilvering was attempted several times but the copper hue always reappeared, until in desperation the dial was painted. Whatever one may think of the ethics of such a conversion, the fact is that this clock can now take its place in a collection, instead of perhaps being relegated to a hidden corner whence it might be lost for ever.

Casework: here we find what are potentially more serious problems. Handles, feet, finials, terminals and other components are broken or lost with the passing of time, although occasionally a minor miracle happens. A friend showed me recently a photograph of a nineteenth-century German bracket clock belonging to her mother. The walnut case is in a reasonable condition for a clock of this age, but the many and various turned-wood finials and terminals are intact and in pristine condition. The explanation was simple. On acquiring the clock from a parent, she had defeated the 'curiosity' of her own young children by taking off all the removable components; these were wrapped, put away and forgotten for years, until a recent spring-cleaning exercise brought them to light and restored the clock to its former glory.

Most clocks are not so fortunate. The Archard clock (photograph 12), for example, has handles of recent origin and the splitting of the case carcase near the original fixing holes suggests that a previous owner attempted to lift the clock by the handles. The replacements are easy to spot; original handles are usually much flimsier and their rings were usually formed from hollow brass tube, bent into a ring and then brazed, whereas replacement rings are usually of solid brass rod.

For finials, terminals and feet, it is possible to obtain a casting, using one of the remaining components as a pattern, but this solution will not be cheap and is worthwhile only if the clock is of merit. An alternative is to purchase a complete set of replacements from a specialist supplier—any newness will be toned down by regular polishing or the intermittent application of medium gold lacquer. An ideal solution is to find replacement components from a clock of the same period, but this can take months, if not years, of patient searching through sundry lots at auction, bric-á-brac stalls at markets and junk shops—I have a couple of clocks that have been waiting patiently for well over a year for components of the correct period and style. The French clock (photograph 21) is an example on which period replacements appear to have been used. A study of this clock revealed that the metal of the flambeau terminal is of slightly different composition and colour than that of the handles and feet; the handles are original to the clock, since many years of 'togetherness' have left their imprint etched into the case sides, and the terminal appears to be of the correct period and style; but the marks beneath the terminal apron suggest that a slightly different shape of apron was originally fitted.

Defects in the timber of the casework are much more of a problem, and may be the deciding factor on whether a clock is accepted or rejected. A seventeenth-century clock in quite poor condition is acceptable, and here I would query the wisdom of *any* restoration, either to the casework or to the dial. Indeed, any casework restoration must to some degree lower the value of the clock: it is up to the buyer to weigh the advantage of having a clock of less value than one in good original condition (and at a higher price) and to accept its defects as they stand, against that of restoring the clock and thereby giving it a new lease of life, with the possible benefit that it will be available to the next generation of collectors.

I have a friend who is a champion of lost causes, specifically those of the German and American shelf clocks of the nineteenth century. Many thousands of these clocks are lost forever because they were made at the lowest possible production cost and were never intended to survive for more than a few years (the beginnings of design for obsolescence?), with the consequence that today few repairers will take on the task of restoration; if they do, the cost is likely to be far more than the clock is worth. My friend will buy such a clock at auction, or rescue one destined for the rubbish-tip, and then spend endless hours rebuilding the whole clock, using whatever materials are available. If necessary he will re-veneer the whole case in a modern timber rather than what may have been American walnut or rosewood, and will then have the front glass panel repainted, if the original is too badly damaged to be touched-in. Some of these clocks could never be described as 'original', but they survive, well cared-for and attractive to behold, and will remain so for years to come. Fifty years into the future, some collector may have reason to thank my friend for maintaining the *character* of such clocks, if not the details. This story has seemed worth telling because I believe that, even in this enlightened age, we are throwing away too many early twentieth-century bracket clocks on the grounds that they are not worth repairing, and we may be throwing away some of our horological history.

Minor faults in the veneer of old cases can be rectified by a skilled cabinetmaker who has a stock of old veneers, but if the case carcase is cracked or split, it may need a complete re-veneering after repairs. It is possible to do this indetectably, using old veneers, but it is a skilled job. The sad fact is that more bracket clock cases get beyond repair than those of most other clocks, since their location and use invite carelessness; visit any antique market and you will find no end of clock movements looking for cases, but rarely will you find a bracket-clock case looking for a movement.

You must expect that any antique bracket clock that you buy will require a certain amount of restoration; how much depends upon what you pay for the clock, and where you buy it from. You have to decide how much restoration will be permissible to maintain, as near as possible, the original state, and whether the work will be worth the expense, relative to the value of the clock.

It is a pity that a section on faking *has* to be included, but in the world of antiques, when a certain area becomes popular, the 'fixers' will always move in to capitalise on a lucrative market. Clocks in general are now enjoying a ready demand and, therefore, examples of faking have followed.

There is the initial argument over what is genuine restoration and what constitutes faking, and there are as many opinions on this subject as there are experts. But having already discussed what I believe to be genuine restoration, I would define faking as a 'deliberate intention to deceive'. Reconverting a recoil escapement back to the crown-wheel type, in a clock that originally had the latter is not faking; but occasionally an original recoil escapement has been converted to the crown-wheel type, simply because the latter commands a much higher price: this is faking. The people who do it would, in another life, be back-winding the speedometer of a secondhand car, the only difference being that fitting a new escapement to a clock is a craftsman's job, requiring skill that should be put to a good, but perhaps less profitable use.

Fortunately, bracket clocks are not as prone to faking as are other clocks (longcases being the favourites), but they are not entirely exempt. I did hear a story of a back plate, signed by John Knibb, that was taken from a scrap clock and grafted on to a more mundane movement of the same period, although it would have had to have been an excellent job of work to escape detection; another story was of a clock bearing a well-known name that was displayed as a centrepiece at a high-class antiques exhibition, while being in fact the product of a Midlands 'renovator', made not 300 years earlier but 3 years earlier. Such stories demonstrate that someone will go to extraordinary lengths to fake a clock if the return justifies the cost.

It is possible to swap bracket-clock movements, although unlike in a longcase, the margins for 'adjustment' are relatively small, considering the size of the average case. If the movement, complete with dial, is transferred, there may have to be alterations to the seatboard or mounting brackets; if a standard movement has been fitted to a clock that originally had a chiming movement, or other feature such as calendar work, there will be signs on the dial of filled-in holes—sometimes only visible under strong light. The filling could have been engraved to match any existing engraving on the dial and a skilled operation could be difficult to detect when access to the back of the dial plate is not possible.

On the subject of engraved dials, the winding holes should not run through the middle of an engraved pattern; nor should a maker's signature be superimposed on what is already a completed pattern. When the clock was being made, the winding holes, maker's name, etc, would have been completed before the engraving was done. Most clockmakers would not engrave their own work—the movement would be despatched to a specialist (probably French or Flemish) once it had been otherwise completed.

With some bracket clocks, the movement from a wall-dial clock could be fitted into the case; this transfer is usually only possible with timepiece movements, since comparatively few of the fusee-driven wall dials were made with strike trains. If this has been done, the winding hole in the original dial may have been elongated slightly, or drilled to a larger diameter, since it would be rare to find a wall-dial movement that would exactly fit the existing dial; another clue to the switch is that the majority of English bracket clocks, up until about 1880, had a pendulum-rod retaining device, for use when the clock was in transit, a device that would not have been fitted to a wall-dial clock.

As in the art world, fake clocks can avoid detection for many years, and the more clocks continue to rise in price, the more will be a temptation to produce what is known in the trade as a 'ringer'—an apt expression when dealing with clocks. There is no effective answer to the skilled forger, except to approach an apparently valuable clock with extreme caution.

CARE AND MAINTENANCE

The average non-clock person has no idea how to handle a pendulum clock. Clocks are frequently brought in for repair with the pendulum still attached and rattling about inside the case; I have watched people picking up clocks in a showroom, turning them this way and that, until the poor pendulum becomes demented and the proprietor has to point out (diplomatically, of course), that this is not the way to handle a clock. I have seen a chiming clock come in for repair at regular intervals because the children of the owner liked to listen to the chimes and often turned the hands back to hear the same chime repeated—we *do* live in a permissive society. Descriptions of clocks in books and magazines are often inaccurate, if not ridiculous, and the treatment meted out to clocks in television programmes is at times disgraceful. During a well-known children's programme, an actor opened the hood of a longcase clock to wind the movement, fitted the key to the striking train instead of the going train, then gave the pendulum a push that would have launched a battleship; it could be heard for the next half-minute or so trying to knock a hole in the sides of the case. One also *sees* early Georgian bracket clocks, but *hears* them chiming the Westminster quarters on gongs; the Westminster chimes (as we know them today) were not in use at that period, and gong striking had not been invented.

So many clocks are damaged, sometimes permanently, when with even a little care they will give years of reliable service. When transporting a pendulum clock over any distance, the pendulum must be removed, otherwise the suspension strip will surely break, or at least develop a kink which will affect its performance. If the pendulum is removed for transit it is sensible to pack the crutch with soft material, such as tissue paper, to prevent it from ticking away at a rapid rate; also, a clock with a strike train is best carried in an upright position. The rack type of strike system operates by gravity, and if the clock begins to strike whilst lying on its side the gathering pallet will not gather, and the strike train will continue to run until the spring power is lost—this event will not cause any serious damage, but it is a bit of a nuisance when the clock is in the boot of your car.

When moving a clock around the home, it is permissible to leave a light pendulum attached. These are usual in later clocks, especially those with gongs or rods mounted across the back plate: more damage can be caused by attempting to manoeuvre the pendulum inside the restricted space than by leaving it in place. As you lift the clock, incline the dial towards you so that the pendulum rod rests against the back plate, thus damping down any movement. Always remove the heavy pendulum of a fusee-drive clock—or use the latch device if fitted.

Never lift a bracket clock by its carrying handles. They may have been functional when the clock was new, but reliance on them to lift an old clock may result in a clock in kit form. Steady the clock with one hand near the top of the case and slide the other hand underneath the case, but be sure you have the correct balance, since some bracket clocks (eg Gothic-arch and full-arch) are surprisingly top-heavy.

One of the worst things that can happen to a clock is that it is made to live in a modern centrally-heated home, where the dry heat dries out the case timber, resulting in splits in the veneer or indeed cracks in the carcase. Remember that case repairs are not only expensive—they are on public view. I am not, or course, advocating that you move house and clocks to the nearest swamp. All that is necessary is to make sure that the atmosphere is not too dry by using commercially-available humidifiers of the simple absorption type, fitted to the heating radiators; even flower vases or other ornaments kept topped up with water will suffice—and will assist your own well-being too! Try, also, to avoid exposing the clock to direct sunlight—museums do not use subdued lighting just for economy reasons. Sunlight will cause most dark woods to fade; you may see an advertisement for a bracket clock in a 'pleasantly faded' case of walnut/rosewood/mahogany, but it would not have been like that when new. Faded hardwoods may co-ordinate well with modern furniture designs, but if you want to restore them to an original finish, it can be quite a task. A good coating of polish will help to retain the moisture in a clock case, and here there is no substitute for tradition. Modern polishes are fine for use on what passes as french polish on modern furniture, but are not as effective on clocks. Certainly the spray polishes should be avoided, since the carrier gas can adversely affect the patina that has built up on the surface of an old clock case; the best finish and protection is obtained with the wax polishes made for use on antique furniture (such as Antiquax)—this, and elbow grease, is all that is necessary.

Dials can be ruined by over-zealous cleaning. Abrasive cleaners, in either liquid form or pad form are out: in no time they will remove the paint from a painted dial or the thin coating of silver compound on a silvered dial. Should a dial require cleaning (and if it does so more than once yearly, I would investigate the root cause) a moistened cloth will do the job, adding a little liquid soap if necessary, to remove an obstinate stain. The glass of the bezel may be cleaned with one of the proprietary window-cleaning fluids, but since most of these contain chemicals, such as DDT, keep them away from the case work. If the brass work of the bezel itself is heavily encrusted with dirt, it may be rubbed down first with one of the abrasive cleaners (avoiding scouring the glass), and from there the wax polish used on the case should keep it 'mellow'.

Having cleaned and sited the clock, let us move on to setting it up and subsequent care. There is probably another law of Parkinson that states that any perfect position for a clock will be found to be unlevel. This is not so important in clocks with crown-wheel escapement, since their wide arc of pendulum swings allows a substantial tolerance—one of the reasons why this escapement remained popular for a portable clock long after the introduction of the more accurate recoil system; but for all other clocks, the level of the surface is critical. (This applies especially to the French and German bracket clocks with their very narrow arc of pendulum swing.) On English and German clocks, the beat can be adjusted by bending the pendulum crutch, but this operation must be carried out with care. It is unwise to bend the crutch by taking hold of the bottom end, then bending it from the pivot at the top end; the correct way is to hold the crutch in a vertical position, with one hand on the pivot (so that you are not exerting any leverage on the pallets and escapement wheel), and bend the lower end a small amount, using fingers or pliers. Refit the pendulum rod, set it swinging and listen to the beat—if it is still awry, repeat the procedure, until the pendulum is beating steadily. (A clock should go 'tock-tock', not 'tick-tock'.) Care should be taken to bend the crutch *sideways* only and not inwards or outwards, as this will affect the pendulum action. Check that the pendulum rod sits freely in the crutch, with clearance between it and the side of the crutch. If, when the clock is beating, there is a 'ghost' click, heard after the pallet has released a wheel tooth, there is probably too much clearance between the pendulum rod and the sides of the crutch; the sound is that of the pendulum rod hitting the side of the crutch as it reverses its swing. The remedy is to squeeze together the arms of the crutch until there is only a slight clearance. A drop of clock oil is permissible at this point—but only a drop.

On French clocks with the roulant movement, the procedure for setting the clock in beat is simplified. Inside the rear case door, there will be two screws, threaded into straps attached to the complete movement, dial and bezel; slacken these screws enough to allow the movement to rotate (by turning the bezel), re-tightening the screws once the clock is in beat. On some clocks, especially those with visible escapements, the anchor of the recoil escapement is a friction fit on its arbor and, therefore, the clock can be set in beat by pushing the pendulum rod to one side or the other. But unless you are sure which type of anchor is fitted, it is wise to adopt one of the former procedures.

When winding a bracket clock, or setting the hands, a few simple precautions are necessary. On the 'round-dial' clocks, such as full-arch and gothic-arch cases, the bezel is often of cast brass, which together with a thick convex glass constitutes a considerable weight to hang from the one hinge. Always support the bezel with one hand, whilst winding or setting with the other. Fit the key carefully to avoid damage to the edges of the winding hole, and do listen for the first 'click' that tells you that the click spring is functioning, before releasing your grip on the key; if it fails to operate, you will be taking the full spring power on the key, in which case it must be slowly unwound (using both hands, if necessary, to maintain contact) until the spring power is released.

Hold the clock hands at the root, rather than the tip, if you need to set them, and turn them clockwise; with some clocks, and with all timepieces, it is possible to turn the hands anti-clockwise, but if you are not certain of the type of movement fitted, or if the clock is a chiming one, turning clockwise is safer. All English striking clocks should have a flexible rack tail which allows for some error (although the flexibility is designed to give safety when the strike train runs down before the going train does so, and not for hand-setting); but sometimes the rack tail has needed repair and, in error, has been replaced by a solid tail. In some French clocks of the late nineteenth century a solid rack tail is a standard component, and in turning the hands back between the 1-o'clock and the 12-o'clock position it is possible to wedge the rack tail into the snail cam. So if in doubt, set the hands clockwise.

On the countwheel strike clock, the hour registered may not agree with the hour struck. If the clock is one of the early types, where the hour hand is screwed to its arbor, lift and release the locking plate, allowing the strike train to run, and repeat the procedure until the correct hour is sounded. This method may also be followed on later German and French clocks, since they used the same system until the early years of the twentieth century. In clocks where the hour hand is a friction fit on its arbor, the hand itself may be moved to register the hour struck: this of course means that the clock does not now register the real time, so it must be stopped or reset until the registered and real time coincide.

EPILOGUE

Given a modicum of care and attention, a bracket clock will give you a lifetime of service. Whether you can afford twenty clocks or just one, the pleasures of ownership will be the same. As you contemplate its beauty of line, and its engineering skill, you will remember that an antique clock has seen more of life than you ever will and try to imagine who first bought it, and what sort of houses and people it has seen during its lifetime. I have a favourite clock, made in about 1760. When I consider that it has lived through Trafalgar, Waterloo, the coming of the railways, steamships, gas and electric lighting, several depressions and two world wars, the old clock takes on far more than its extrinsic value—it becomes a chronicle of history.

Collecting bracket clocks brings a continual learning process. No book can be a substitute for experience, or convey the gamut of emotions that the pursuit will bring: the longing looks at museum pieces, the thrill of the chase after some desirable specimen, the dejection when it turns out not to be so, the despair of buying a clock with unforeseen faults, the comfortable complacency of routine maintenance of a cherished example. I hope to have imparted just something of the magic of these clocks, whether they are new to you or this book is simply rekindling old experiences.

DATING BRACKET CLOCKS

The charts that follow are intended as a rapid reference to a particular clock. By cross-reference the researcher should be able to build up a reasonably complete picture of what a specific clock should have in the way of case style, dial, type of movement, construction materials etc.

Other books dealing with bracket clocks include: *English House Clocks 1600–1850*, by Anthony Bird (David & Charles 1973); *English Domestic Clocks* by H. Cescinsky and M. R. Webster (Antique Collectors' Club, reprinted 1976) and, for clocks from 1840 onwards, *The Price Guide to Clocks 1840–1940* by Alan and Rita Shenton (Antique Collectors' Club, 1976). A 'companion' book, to study the development of the longcase clock during the period 1760–1850, is the excellent *White Dial Clocks* by Brian Loomes (David & Charles, new edition 1981).

Periodicals include, for the more technically minded, *Horological Journal* (British Horological Institute) and *Antiquarian Horology* (Antiquarian Horological Society); both offer membership services. *Clocks* magazine is invaluable because it provides an enquiry service.

Any knowledge so gained must be useful, especially as the field of antiquarian horology is so new; as clocks become more of an archaeological area, research will intensify and many existing theories may be revised. The story of bracket-clock development is not finished, since with every discovery it is either amplified or confused. The collector of the future will have the same problems as those of today, when he tries to piece together the story of a bracket clock of the 1980s; when he eventually determines the total number of these clocks produced, his initial belief that the German mechanical and electronic movements of the 1980s killed off the British makers might have to be changed. Both he and we must, as I have tried to do, see the clocks against the background of the events of their times, the technological and economic considerations that, evolved manufacturers of, and markets for, the bracket clock.

While development and research continue, the origins of the bracket clock are still unclear. I have had to start before the first one recorded, since its components had been developed for other clocks. Many of the early records are lost forever, and today's 'knowledge' is necessarily a mixture of fact and surmise. Fortunately, from 1650 onwards enough clocks have survived to build up a reasonable picture, and many of these have authenticated dates to provide the factual basis for a development theory. Certain events also fit this basis, since they were of such significance that they are well recorded. No one would dispute the date, to within five years or so, of the invention of the recoil escapement, for instance, or of the rack striking mechanism. Similarly, as we move into the nineteenth century, there are many records surviving that detail not only the clocks themselves, but serial numbers, prices and the names of customers; most of these are ledgers or day-books.

The dating of case styles is one of the more difficult areas because some styles died slowly and were still being produced long after the introduction of new models; the history of movement details, such as escapements and engraving work, is similarly indeterminate, as some buyers have always preferred traditional methods and would pay a premium for a product of individual quality. This is why one will find an engraved back plate on a clock of 1850 when in theory such work had vanished from general use by 1810—the advantage, of course, is that the clock will be a quality specimen, whether or not it fits the pattern.

So the dating charts that follow contain not only 'solid' lines to indicate periods when a feature was in general use, but also 'dotted' lines to show features sometimes used at a date when they had generally been superseded or had not yet come into general use.

Terminology is also a problem. Clockmakers' records describe clocks in terms relevant only at that time; nowadays we may have to use a different term in order to distinguish that particular style from one that came later. An example of this is the term 'round top', in common use around 1800 to describe what we now call a 'full-arch' case as we have to distinguish it from its near-cousin the 'break-arch' top and, more remotely, the 'balloon' case.

Then, exactly what were the Georgian, Regency or Victorian periods? Some authors suggest that the Georgian period runs from 1714 (the accession of George I) to 1820 (death of George III). They discount George IV, claiming that as Prince Regent his times should be included in the Regency period, not the Georgian; but in that case the Regency period continues up until 1830, ten years after the title of Prince Regent had ceased to exist. In strict terms, the Georgian period runs from 1714 to 1830, with the Regency period slotted in, between 1800 and 1820. However, it is convenient to use the former definitions because the dates denote changes in general furniture styles. (Some references clarify this situation by using the term 'true Regency' to denote 1800–20.)

This book *must* contain both facts and personal opinions, but the charts are designed to summarise the facts, as far as possible.

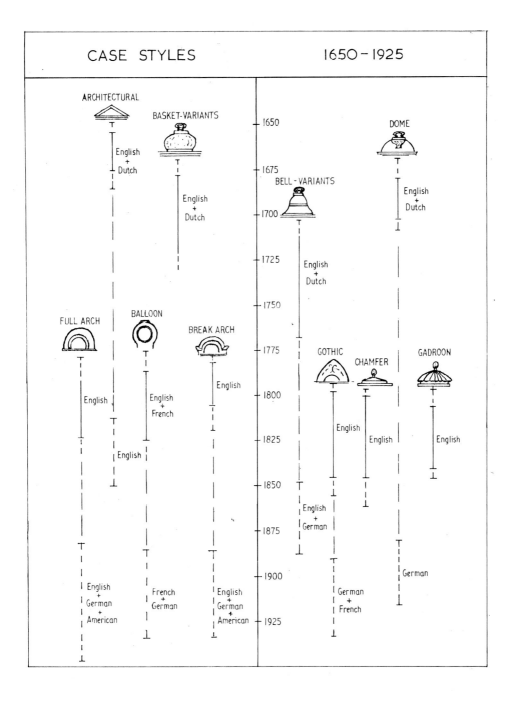

CASE STYLES — 1650–1925

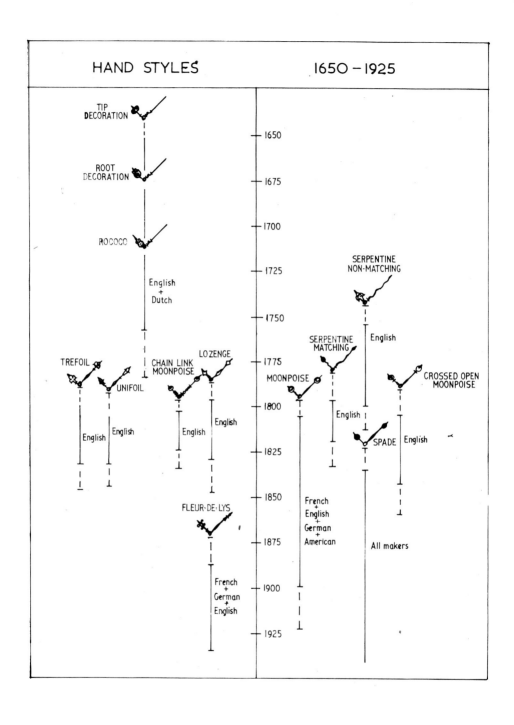

HAND STYLES   1650 – 1925

TIP
DECORATION

ROOT
DECORATION

ROCOCO

English
+
Dutch

TREFOIL   CHAIN LINK   LOZENGE
                 MOONPOISE
       UNIFOIL

English   English   English   English

                 FLEUR·DE·LYS

                 French
                 +
                 German
                 +
                 English

SERPENTINE
NON-MATCHING

SERPENTINE
MATCHING   English

MOONPOISE   CROSSED OPEN
                                 MOONPOISE

                 English

                      SPADE   English

French
+
English
+
German
+
American   All makers

1650
1675
1700
1725
1750
1775
1800
1825
1850
1875
1900
1925

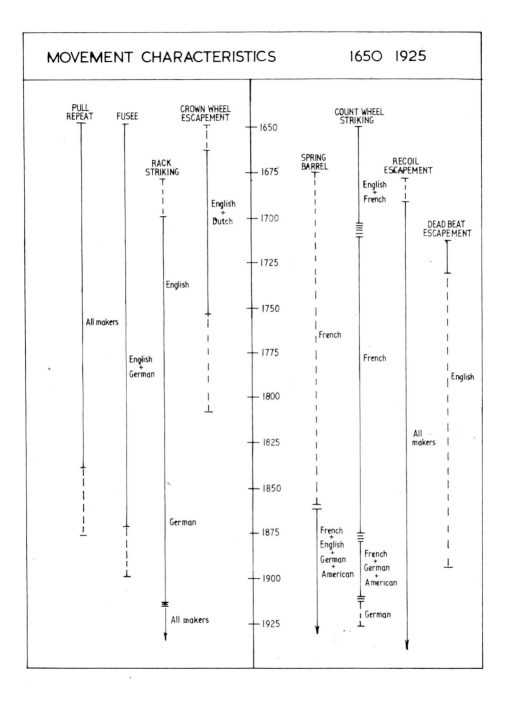

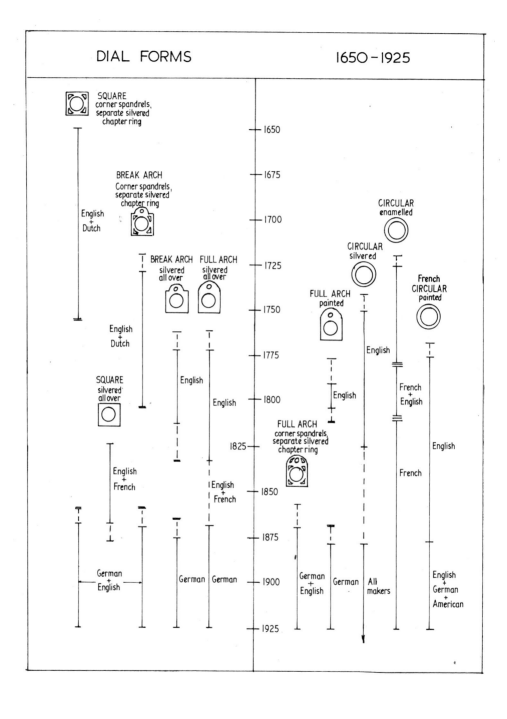

DIAL FORMS   1650–1925

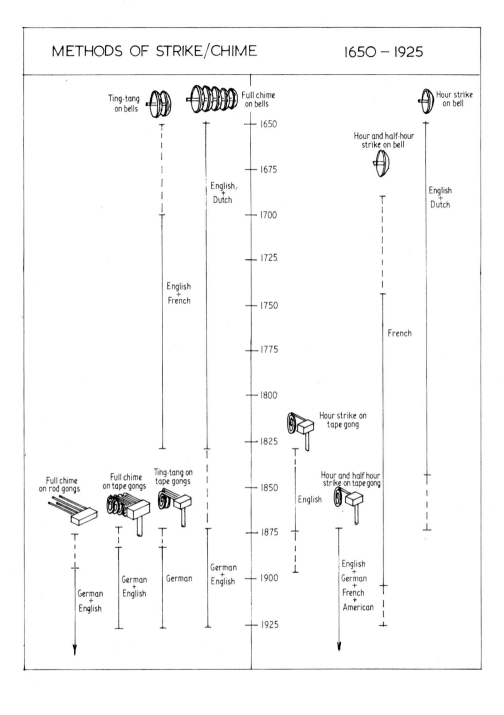

METHODS OF STRIKE/CHIME   1650 – 1925

Ting-tang on bells

Full chime on bells

Hour strike on bell

Hour and half-hour strike on bell

1650

1675

English + Dutch

English + Dutch

1700

1725

English + French

1750

1775

French

1800

Hour strike on tape gong

1825

Full chime on rod gongs

Full chime on tape gongs

Ting-tang on tape gongs

Hour and half hour strike on tape gong

1850

English

German + English

German

German + English

1875

German + English

English + German + French + American

1900

1925

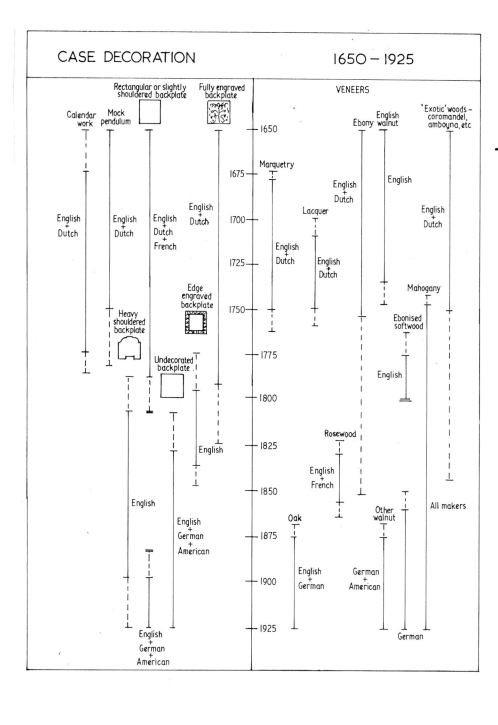

CASE DECORATION   1650 – 1925

CLOCKMAKERS, MONARCHS AND FURNITURE STYLES 1650–1925

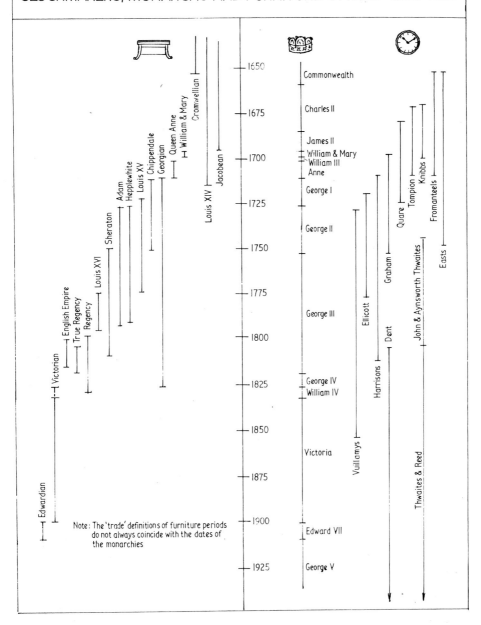

1650 — Commonwealth

1675 — Charles II

James II
1700 — William & Mary
William III
Anne

George I

1725 —

George II

1750 —

1775 —

George III

1800 —

1825 — George IV
William IV

1850 —

Victoria

1875 —

1900 —

Edward VII

1925 — George V

Cromwellian
Louis XIV
Jacobean
William & Mary
Queen Anne
Georgian
Chippendale
Louis XV
Hepplewhite
Adam
Sheraton
Louis XVI
Regency
True Regency
English Empire
Victorian
Edwardian

Fromanteels
Knibbs
Tompion
Quare
Easts
Graham
John & Aynsworth Thwaites
Ellicott
Dent
Harrisons
Vuillamys
Thwaites & Reed

Note: The 'trade' definitions of furniture periods do not always coincide with the dates of the monarchies

APPENDIX A:
FUSEE DESIGN

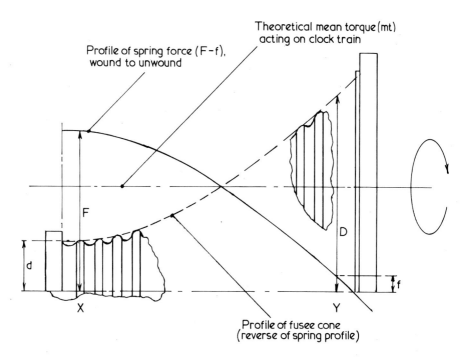

Theoretical mean torque (mt)
acting on clock train

Profile of spring force (F–f),
wound to unwound

Profile of fusee cone
(reverse of spring profile)

mt should remain constant throughout spring range; therefore the ideal equation would be:

$$(F \rightarrow f) \times (d \rightarrow D) = mt \times C$$
$$\text{So, at point } x, \ F \times d = mt$$
$$\text{at point } y, \ f \times D = mt$$

APPENDIX B:
RELATIVE POWER OUTPUTS
OF CLOCK DRIVES

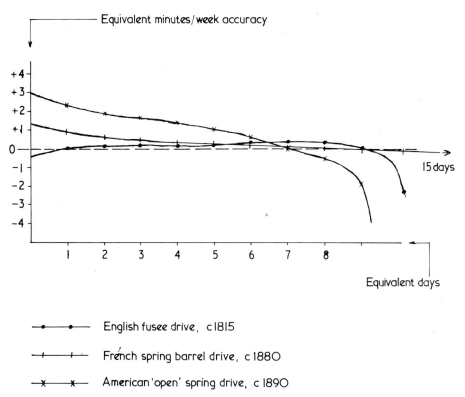

———•———•——— English fusee drive, c 1815

———+———+——— French spring barrel drive, c 1880

———x———x——— American 'open' spring drive, c 1890

Note The actual torque, measured at the great wheel, gives no indication of its effect on timekeeping, since the gear trains of the clocks measured exhibit widely varying characteristics. To provide a comparison, the measured torque has been converted, by estimation, into the equivalent of minutes/week fast or slow.

ACKNOWLEDGEMENTS

The author wishes to thank the following people for their help: Penny Paterson, for sympathetic photography of the clocks shown on the jacket and in photographs 12, 13, 16, 18, 21, 26, 27, 28, 29; D. T-D. Clarke (Colchester and . Essex Museum Service), for helpful advice and permission to use the clocks shown on the jacket and in photographs 8, 9, 10, 11, 14, 15; John Steel (Antique Collectors' Club), for permission to use photographs 20, 22, 23, 24, 25; Edward Corcoran, for permission to use the clock shown in photograph 16; M. Harding (Sinclair, Harding & Co), for permission to use photograph 30; T. A. Camerer Cuss (Camerer, Cuss & Co), for permission to use the clock shown in photograph 17; Trinity Clocks, Colchester, for permission to use the clock shown in photographs 18 and 19; the British Museum, for permission to use the photographs 1 (a and b), 2, 3, 7 (a and b); The Victoria & Albert Museum, for permission to use photograph 6; The Science Museum, for permission to use photographs 4 and 5; Arthur Little, *Clocks Magazine*, for the help of his research department; C. J. Webb (E. Dent & Co), for details on the history of Dent's; E. J. Buckingham, for advice, recollections and entertaining arguments concerning B. Vulliamy; Hazel Homewood, for her typing services.

INDEX

Act of Parliament, 75, 76
Adam, Robert, 82
American clocks, 18, 121
Anchor escapement (*see* Recoil)
Archard, London, 91, 92, 97

Backplates, 186
Balance-wheel, 14, 25, 54, 106
Banister, Joseph, 88
Barlow, Edward, 10, 39
Barrel, spring, 18
Bell strike, 120
Boulle, Andre Charles, 66, 67
Breguet, Abraham-Louis, 91
Brocot, Achille, 108, 120

Calendar work, 51, 53, 78
Case styles (*see also* Tables)
  architectural, 44, 46
  balloon, 82, 83
  basket, 48
  bell-top, true, 49; inverted,
    50, 58, 63
  break-arch, 61, 72, 73, 140
  chamfer top, 89, 103
  full-arch, 74, 91, 116, 136
  gadroon, 89, 90, 103, 104
  Gothic arch, 84–9, 103, 135
  waisted, 67, 82, 83
Chapter ring, 13
Chimes
  Cambridge, 131
  Holy Trinity, 131, 132
  St Michael's, 132, 133, 134
  Ting-tang, 53, 122, 124, 125,
    138
  Westminster, 131, 134, 144,
    146, 147, 149
  Whittington, 133, 134, 149
Chiming systems, 125–34
Chippendale, 71, 72
Clepsydra, 10, 14, 15, 16
Clockmakers Company, 29–31

Clockmaking in:
  America, 37
  France, 37, 66, 67, 83, 106,
    118, 120, 121
  Germany, 37, 121
  Holland, 65, 66
  Italy, 13, 14
  Nuremburg, 13, 14
Clock springs, 17–23
Congreve, Sir William, 94, 95
Control systems for clocks,
  25–35
Cooper, John, 100, 101, 102
Coster, Salomon, 10, 30
Countwheel striking, 14, 35–7,
  120, 183
Crown-wheel escapement 32–5,
  55

Da Vinci, Leonardo, 22
Dead-beat escapement, 11, 59,
  60
Dent and Co, 148
Dent, Edward John, 110
Dial styles (*see also* Tables)
  break-arch, 60, 61, 63
  circular, 69, 71
  early, 46, 49, 50, 55, 58
  full-arch, 72, 103, 140
  painted, 73
  silvered, 137
  stove-enamelled, 73, 118, 169

East, Edward, 29, 31
Edge engraving, 78, 93, 186
Ellicott, John, 69, 71
Elliot and Co, 150
Empire designs, 89, 91
Enfield Clock Co, 146, 147
Escapements
  crown-wheel, 32–5, 55
  dead-beat, 11, 59, 60
  recoil, 10, 37–9, 40, 55

  terminology, 32
  verge, 32
  visible, 108

Foliot, 14, 25
French bracket clocks, 8, 9, 19,
  99, 115, 119, 121
Fromanteel, Ahasuerus, 8, 16,
  28–31
Fromanteel, John, 30
Fusee
  application, 21, 22
  design, 22–5, 188
  lines, 23, 24

Galileo, 10, 26
Garrard Clock Co, 146
German clocks, 18, 121, 141
Gongs
  tape, 108
  rod, 132, 133
Graham, George, 11, 55–60,
  68, 69, 70
Gregorian calendar, 12
Grid-iron pendulum, 11, 68, 70

Hamburg America Clock Co,
  145
Hand styles
  chain-link moonpoise, 91
  crossed open spade, 78
  cross moonpoise, 78
  early, 46, 49, 55, 88
  fleur-de-lys, 119, 120, 122,
    138
  moonpoise, 78, 90
  serpentine, 71, 116
  spade, 90
  trefoil, 89, 114
  unifoil, 89
Harrison, John, 11, 68, 69, 70
Hedge and Banister, 85–8
Hedge family, 80, 81

Hedge, John, 76–81
Hepplewhite, 72
Hooke, Dr Robert, 37, 69
Hope, Thomas, 82, 83, 84, 91, 116
Hopper, William, 84
Huygens, 10

Japy Frères, 120, 121
Jones, Henry, 44, 45

Lacquer work, 50
Lancet-top case (see Case styles, Gothic)
Lantern clocks, 10
Lenzkirch, 138, 139
Locking plate (see Countwheel)

Mantel regulators, 60
Marble clock cases, 47, 48, 82, 98, 99, 102, 103, 109, 112, 124, 135, 137
Markwick, James, 62, 63
Mason Collection, The, 89
Mercury pendulum, 68, 69, 70
Moon-phase work, 61

Nash, John, 84

Oiling of clocks, 159

Pareto rule, 47
Pendulum
  bob, 31, 33
  cycloidal cheeks, 28
  design, 25–8
  Galileo's 26

grid-iron, 11, 68, 70
Huygens', 27
isochronous, 26
mercury, 68, 69, 70
Power source, 17, 189
Pull-repeat, 53, 55, 64, 93, 106, 114

Quare, Daniel, 50, 51, 52, 54

Rack striking, 39–42, 183
Ramsey, Devonport, 112, 113
Rayment, John, 63, 64
Recoil escapement, 10, 37–9, 55
Roulant movement, 120, 121, 177
Rowley, A. & H., 116, 117

Sand glass, 10, 14, 15, 16
Sheraton, 74, 135
Sidereal time, 12
Sinclair, Harding and Bazeley, 148, 149
Solar day, 12
Spring
  faults, 20, 21
  in fusee drive, 22, 23
  manufacture, 19–20
Stackfreed, 10, 21
Star wheel, 53, 93, 114
Stop-work, 24
Strike/silent, mechanism, 58, 60, 114
Striking mechanisms
  countwheel, 14, 35–7, 120, 183

rack, 39–42, 183
Sundial, 14

Tables
  Backplates, 186
  Case styles, 181
  Dial forms, 184
  Escapements, 183
  Furniture styles, 187
  Hand styles, 182
  Methods of strike chime, 185
  Monarchs, 187
  Movements, 183
  Striking mechanisms, 183
  Veneers, 186
Thwaites and Reed, 93–7
Thwaites, John, 93
Tompion, Thomas, 55, 59
Torque, 22
Transition clocks, 142–7

Up-and-down work, 58, 108, 122

Veneer for cases, 64-5, 74, 75, 172, 186
Verge, 10
Vulliamy, Benjamin Louis, 106, 107, 110, 111

Westminster, Great Clock of, 110
Winterhalder and Hofmeyer, 122, 123, 134
Wright, London, 104, 105

Yonge, George, 98